WHAT

WHEN YOU ~~DON'T~~
WHAT TO DO

Trusting Christ When Life Gets Confusing

Adult Journal

*Dedicated to Doug and Sharon Worden,
who have repeatedly encouraged us in our efforts to follow Christ when
life got confusing.*

CONTENTS

Introduction 3

How to Use This Journal 5

Action Step Descriptions 7

Action Step Summary 12

Adventuring with Family and Friends 13

Warm-up Days 17

Days 1–13 20

Prayer Partner Sessions 34

Prayer Partner Covenant 35

Days 14–18 36

Daily Joy Tracker 40

Days 19–50 42

Follow-up Day 75

This journal was created with input from more than 30 pastors and laypersons from across North America.

Writing team: David R. Mains, Director; Patric Knaak, Marian Oliver, Randy Petersen, Mitchell Vander Vorst

Editor: Marian Oliver
Assistant Editor: Mitchell Vander Vorst
Cover Illustration: Joe VanSeveren
Cover Design: Tony Laidig
Text Design: Blum Graphic Design

Copyright © 1995 *The Chapel Ministries, Inc.*
Published by *The Chapel Ministries*
Dr. David R. Mains, Director

All Scripture quotations, unless otherwise indicated, are taken from the HOLY BIBLE, NEW INTERNATIONAL VERSION®. NIV®. Copyright©1973, 1978, 1984 by International Bible Society. Used by permission of Zondervan Publishing House. All rights reserved.

Scripture quotations from THE MESSAGE are used by permission of NavPress Publishing Group. Copyright©1993.

The Chapel Ministries is a nonprofit, nondenominational, international Christian outreach dedicated to helping God's church grow spiritually and numerically by revitalizing its members, whether they be gathered or scattered, to be a force for kingdom purposes worldwide. To support this goal, The Chapel Ministries provides print and media resources including the annual 50-Day Spiritual Adventure and 4-Week Worship Celebration, the daily half-hour television program "You Need to Know," and seasonal radio programming. Year-round Bible study guides are offered through a Joint Ministry Venture with Scripture Union U.S.A., to encourage the healthy spiritual habits of daily Scripture reading and prayer.

Printed in the United States of America

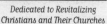
Dedicated to Revitalizing Christians and Their Churches

ISBN 1-879050-70-6

NTRODUCTION

ICTURE YOURSELF at the entrance to a maze. A voice is calling you from somewhere inside, but how do you get there? Which path do you choose?

You head off to the right and almost immediately face a fork in the road. Which y should you go? You take the path to the left, which turns a corner and dead-ds. You retrace your steps, try other paths, encounter new options, and go on.

Before long your sense of direction gets clouded. You're lost and confused. Have u tried this way before or not? Is there any hope of reaching the voice that calls d calls?

You probably know the feeling. You've had days and weeks when you just did not ow what to do, when you feared there was no way through the maze of your life.

Perhaps you identify with some of these questions. What is God's plan for me and ▼ family? How am I going to find the time for everything I need to do? Will my life ange as I grow older? What is my importance in this world? Am I on the right path is it a diversion? Why does it seem that so many bad things are happening? What out divorce, personal loss, financial uncertainty? Maybe your questions stem from ense that God is calling you to move forward, to do something significant for him. t how do you get there? How do you move through the confusion?

This 50-Day Spiritual Adventure is designed to help you deal with your confusion. st, you need to focus on what you truly believe. Is it your conviction that God truly res for you, and that he will guide you through your maze? Proverbs 3:6 advises, "In your ways acknowledge him, and he will make your paths straight." Acknowledge ur trust in the Lord with a daily prayer, and regularly review his promises. Join with hers in talking about your situation. Look for the joys God gives you each day— en in the middle of your muddle. Take specific steps to clear away the clutter of ur life, to simplify things so that you can serve God more freely and fully.

During this Adventure you'll explore eight topics that should help you trust Christ confusing times.

opic 1: Choose to believe Christ will make a way for you through the maze

opic 2: Embrace the great promises of God's Word

opic 3: Pursue support relationships with other believers

opic 4: Look for the joys that refresh your spirit

opic 5: Remove unnecessary confusion from your life

opic 6: Accept the Lord's grace and forgiveness

opic 7: Discover how Jesus identifies with your struggles

opic 8: Place your hope in the God of surprising outcomes

Confusion is a fact of life, but so is God's guidance. You will often face times hen you don't know what to do. As you trust Christ, he will bring clarity to your e and lead you joyfully through the maze.

INDIA AND NEPAL JOIN THE ADVENTURE TEAM

COMMON PICTURES that come to mind when we think about India are the Taj Mahal, elephants and tigers, people bathing in the river Ganges, or a Hindu temple. Nepal brings visions of Mount Everest and the bright colored bazaars of Kathmandu.

But for Christians in India and Nepal, the picture is one of spiritual harvest. While Nepal is 98 percent Hindu and Buddhist, the Christian church is growing. In India baptisms are common, and congregations are springing up in previously unreached villages. In both countries well-trained nationals are boldly crossing age-old barriers of language and culture to serve as missionaries in their own land.

Christ's church is flourishing in India and Nepal. This has become a land where old men dream dreams, and young men have visions of a bumper harvest.

While you are involved in this year's 50-Day Spiritual Adventure in North America, hundreds of thousands of brothers and sisters in India and Nepal will also participate in this program of accelerated spiritual growth. They will measure their progress by keeping a daily journal adapted to their language and setting. They'll practice good spiritual disciplines just as you will, and hopefully those habits will last well beyond Day 50. Believers will hear Adventure sermons in their churches and related radio programs called "The Spiritual Journey," broadcast in eight languages over Trans World Radio.

These Christians are aware that in North America you also are learning about what to do when you don't know what to do. They will be praying for you even though they don't know you by name.

So during the Adventure be conscious of this international linkage. Remember the church on this Indian subcontinent, rich in a history that stretches back to the time of Thomas, one of the original Twelve who traditionally is recognized as the first to evangelize their land. And pray that this will be a wonderful time of continued growth for the church.

HOW TO USE THIS JOURNAL

WE ARE EXPECTING that one million people will join you in this Spiritual Adventure. Like you, they'll set aside 50 days to focus on trusting Christ when life gets confusing. This unique study should prove to be a time of refreshment, renewal, and accelerated growth for individuals and churches alike. The Adventure involves five action steps, or spiritual disciplines, that you'll be doing throughout the 50 days. By incorporating these action steps into your daily routine, you will develop godly habits as you trust the Holy Spirit to work in your life.

One of the action steps involves praying a simple but powerful prayer each day. We've provided a sample for you to use as a guide. What better way to trust Christ than to regularly affirm your belief in his care. Another of the action steps is to study Scripture daily, concentrating on the marvelous promises God gives to strengthen your faith. All five action steps are explained in detail on pages 7–11.

Once you've familiarized yourself with the five action steps, all you need to do to complete this Adventure is follow the journal each day. In addition to the Scripture readings and questions, you'll find daily reminders to help you keep up with the other assignments. For a quick overview of where you've been and where you're headed each week, see the "Looking Back . . . Looking Ahead" pages, usually after each Friday journal page. Journal-keeping is a proven way to measure your growth. You may want to look back in a couple of weeks and remind yourself of the ways you've grown in trusting Christ through your confusion.

Each topic is introduced with a format different from the other journal pages. There is a commentary by David Mains which will explain the theme for the days that follow. The graphic icons will give you a quick way of identifying the various tasks.

For each of the topics you will also want to read the appropriate chapter in the Adventure guidebook *When Life Becomes a Maze: Discovering Christ's Resources for Times of Confusion* by David Mains. This book will provide you with inspiration for the Adventure and take you deeper into each of the topics. Contact your church, your local Christian bookstore, or The Chapel Ministries for your copy (see p. 19).

Many people find they want to pursue some of the Adventure topics in even greater depth. So we've suggested additional resources to help you customize the Adventure to meet your

needs. On each "Looking Back . . . Looking Ahead" page, you'll find optional follow-up scriptures and a recommended book for further study. We've reviewed dozens of titles and believe these to be the best available on the Adventure topics. We commend them to you as a way to fully personalize this series.

You'll need to set aside 10 to 15 minutes a day for this Adventure. Some of the action steps will take a little extra effort, but they come up only a few times during the 50 days. If you plan on following the Adventure as a family or with one or more friends, you will probably need to allow more time. On pages 13–16 you'll find suggestions for making the most of that special time. We are certain that the benefits will be well worth your investment.

Experts claim that it takes about 21 days to form a habit—good or bad. So this 50-Day Adventure should give you ample time to establish spiritual habits that will continue beyond Day 50. And if after 50 days you're looking for a way to keep some of the disciplines going, we have a great idea for you on page 76.

It may help you to keep track of everything by filling in the date in the space provided for each day. If you fall behind please don't give up or get discouraged. You don't need to go over what you missed. Just get back on track with the current day's assignment. God is always ready to give you a fresh start and strengthen you as you press on in your journey.

An adventure is always easier and more exciting when you team up with someone else. Being accountable is a good way to make sure you get the most out of these 50 days. Consider joining with a fellow believer or group of believers (or with the prayer partners you choose for Action Step 3), and encourage one another along the way. How exciting it is if your entire church is doing the study. Ask a fellow congregation member to pray for you and check on your progress regularly. Offer to do the same for him or her.

Another source of encouragement is the "You Need to Know" television program (the 1995 National Religious Broadcasters Television Program of the Year). Aired Monday through Friday, these special Adventure shows will give you insights into the topics and Scripture readings for each day. Don't miss them. To find out when "You Need to Know" is aired in your area, call your local Christian TV station or The Chapel Ministries at 1-800-224-2735. The Adventure will also be aired on participating radio stations.

Take a few minutes now to prepare for the Adventure.

START BY FAMILIARIZING yourself with the five action steps. Read pages 7–11. It will also be helpful to flip through the day-to-day pages of the journal starting on page 17. This way you will have an idea of what will be coming. Then on the Friday before Day 1 of the Adventure, begin the Warm-up Day exercises (p. 17) to give you a head start.

Our prayer is that God will be in these 50 days in such a freeing way that you will delight in trusting him as he lifts you above life's confusion and draws you to himself.

Do Daily
Fill Your Days with "I Believe" Statements

WHAT DO YOU BELIEVE? If you're a Christian, certainly you can cite some appropriate Bible truths: I believe God created the world; I believe Christ died for my sins; I believe Christ is the Head of the church.

These are wonderful points of faith, but what do they mean in your life? Do your beliefs affect the way you work, the way you relax, the way you live? Do your beliefs have an effect on your emotions, or on your decisions? When life gets confusing, do your beliefs encourage you and help you think more clearly? Sometimes when we're confused we forget what we really believe. We get our priorities tangled and major on the minors, or we worry needlessly. We can begin to clear away the fog by going back to the basics.

What do you believe? Do you believe in a loving, powerful God? Do you believe he wants what's best for you, and offers guidance, and provides many joys along the way? Too many Christians recite litanies of worry and doubt: "Oh, dear, not again! Nothing ever goes right for me!" Let us instead be "I believe" people, asserting our confidence that God is doing great things in our lives.

Instructions:

EACH DAY CONCENTRATE ON THE TRUTHS and promises you believe. Look at the promise scriptures in the journal (usually on Fridays) or the *Believe It Or Not Promise Pack* (see p. 19), or let Scripture guide you in making a list of your own. Then let those beliefs become a vital part of your daily life. As you think about your confusion make an "I believe" statement using one of God's promises. For example, say Romans 8:28 to yourself or others, *"I believe that in all things God works for the good of those who love him."* Get in the habit of stating that you're an "I believe" person.

The "I Believe" Prayer (below) will help you stay focused. Fill in the blank with a promise from Scripture. Say it at least once a day. It may be good to establish a regular time to say the prayer, perhaps just after you wake up, or before you go to bed. But don't limit the prayer to those times. Take it with you and pray it whenever you need to—on your coffee break, at the gas station, or anytime during the day.

As with any written prayer, you need to make it your own. There's no magic in these words. Be sure to pray it from your heart, in your own way of speaking.

The "I Believe" Prayer

Father,

Sometimes I feel confused and don't understand why things happen the way they do.

Yet I believe you love me deeply, and absolutely nothing is beyond your control.

Help me to live each day with confidence, trusting in the great promises of your Word.

Today I am reminded _____ *(fill in promise)* _____ .

Thank you for giving me the strength to be an "I believe" person. Amen.

■■■■■■■ ·■■■■■■ ·■■■■■■ ·■■■■■■ ·■■■■■■ ·■■■■■■ ·■■■■■■■■■

● ACTION STEP 2

Do Daily
Face Confusion with Confidence from God's Word

YOU'RE FLYING IN A JETLINER, and when the pilot introduces himself you realize it's an old friend. You mention this to the attendant, and soon you're invited forward to the cockpit. Your friend the pilot shows you the assortment of instruments and says, "Here. Why don't you fly it for a while?"

He cajoles you into taking his seat and he hovers over your shoulder giving instructions. "Watch that dial now. Press the lever there. Good, now keep it steady." It's a tense time, but you're not worried. Why not? You're at the helm of a huge hunk of metal, ferrying hundreds of people through thin air, and you have no clue! But your friend the pilot has all the answers you need.

Yet what if he says, "I'm going back for a cup of coffee," and leaves you alone in the cockpit? Then it's panic time! You don't know which buttons to push and which to leave alone. Your head is awhirl with confusion and fear. You desperately need guidance.

As we fly through life, God is our friendly pilot. We may be clueless, confused by the many situations in our life, but he knows what to do. We can be confident in the directions and assurances he gives us in his Word. Our loving Lord has promised to stay with us, to guide us, and never to disappear for a cup of coffee (see Psalm 32:8).

Instructions:

FOR EACH DAY OF THE ADVENTURE READ the assigned Scripture passage and answer the questions in this journal. (Saturday and Sunday are usually treated as one day.) Many of the questions are open-ended and intended to make you think. There is not always a right or wrong answer. Each week the scriptures center on a new topic, all relating to "What to Do When You Don't Know What to Do."

Every week (usually on Friday), there is a well-chosen promise scripture that corresponds to the topic. Take special time with these promises. Make them part of your "mental grid."

Here are further options to seriously consider:
● Commit these promises to memory. What a great help they'll be when you're in the middle of a maze.

● Make it a point to quote or give a paraphrase of these promises to someone you see during the day. This way you are taking ownership of them.

● Get the *Believe It Or Not Promise Pack,* which includes all eight of these promises (and eight more), printed on handy cards. Carry these with you and review them during the day, or post them on a mirror or refrigerator—someplace where you'll see them regularly and be reminded of the pertinent truths they express. (To obtain a Promise Pack see p. 19.)

Do Four Times
Unleash the Power of Prayer Partnerships

A MAN BOUGHT a new stereo system: CD player, dual cassette, AM-FM tuner, equalizer, and state-of-the-art speakers. It was a fabulous set of machinery, with more lights and digital displays than one could ever want or need. One problem: It didn't work.

So he called his buddy—the one who was always tinkering with electronic gadgets. Surely this guy would figure out the problem; maybe he could even fix it.

The electronics whiz came over, studied the stereo, and walked around it hemming and hawing. Then he plugged it in. The stereo worked perfectly.

Sometimes it takes an extra pair of eyes. Sometimes our confusion stems from something as simple as an unplugged plug. When we get together with others and talk about our difficulties, we just might find a new way of looking at things or some much-needed support.

Our friends may be just as confused as we are. But at least we'll be together as we take our confusion to the Lord. Talk about plugging in to a power source! Christ promised to be with us in a special way when we gather with one or two others in his name (Matthew 18:19–20).

What do you do when you don't know what to do? Find a friend, and together take your concerns to the Lord.

Instructions:

S ELECT ONE OR TWO other Christians as prayer partners and meet with them four times during the Adventure. These half-hour meetings could occur over the phone, but preferably they're face to face. When you get together, you can have a few minutes of casual catch-up, but move quickly into the sharing of your prayer requests and joys, and be sure to spend a good amount of time actually praying. Choose prayer partners with whom you feel comfortable sharing your confusion, with whom you can be honest and vulnerable.

Follow the instructions on page 34. They provide specific guidelines for each session.

THE WAGNERS STRUCK UPON A SURE-FIRE WAY TO GET
THE NEIGHBORS TOGETHER FOR AN HOUR OF BIBLE STUDY.

Do Daily
Energize Your Faith by Tracking Daily Joys

REMEMBER PAC-MAN? This video game of the early '80s involved a little round creature who gobbled up dots to earn points while chased by four shrouded villains. But there were four "power pills" placed around the screen, and when Pac-Man ate one of these, he was energized to gobble up the villains. The bad guys would scurry away until the power pill's effects wore off.

Life is a little like Pac-Man. There are various worries and doubts that chase us around. But then there are good things that happen—joyous events that energize us for a while, chasing the worries away.

Sometimes we get so wrapped up in confusion that we overlook the good things that happen. We are so concerned about our struggles, our worries, our doubts, that we miss the joys. Yet the apostle Paul urges believers to "rejoice always" (Philippians 4:4). When we take time to see the positives, we gain strength to deal with the negatives.

This is not just some kind of "positive thinking" gimmick, to look at life through rose-colored glasses. We want to look at life realistically, but we want to make sure we don't miss the blessings God keeps sending our way.

Instructions:

LOOK FOR A "JOY" each day of the Adventure and write it down in the Daily Joy Tracker on pages 40–41. You're looking for evidence of God's care. It may be an act of kindness someone showed you, an answered prayer, a surprising gift, a letter from a friend, a good night's rest, or even a satisfying meal. What brings joy to your life on that particular day? Choose one thing to write down each day.

Except Wednesday. Each Wednesday, your mission is to bring joy to someone else. Write a note of appreciation. Send flowers. Play a gentle prank. Tell a joke. Or just let someone know how much you care. Jot down in the Daily Joy Tracker what you did and for whom.

PASTOR WAGMAN KNEW HE WAS ON A ROLL
WHEN THE CONGREGATION STARTED DOING THE WAVE.

ACTION STEP 5

Do Three Times
Find Three Ways to Unclutter Your Life

JACKIE SEEMS LIKE SUPERMOM, ferrying her kids from soccer practice to piano lessons, leading a women's Bible study at church, keeping a crisp house, and holding down a nearly full-time job. But she's quietly going crazy, wondering why she does what she does, and whether it's all worth it. It's getting harder to keep up the pace.

Bob owns his own business. It has grown, and so have his responsibilities. Though he now has half a dozen employees, he still insists on checking every bank statement, reviewing inventory, and writing ad copy. He works from early morning to late at night, but he will not delegate. It seems more and more difficult to keep control.

Arlene has had trouble sleeping lately. She worries. How long will she have a job? What will happen if the mortgage payment on the house can't be paid? Has she done everything possible to ensure an orderly and happy life without surprises?

You may recall a biblical scene: Martha scurrying about the kitchen, fussing over a million details, pausing only to complain that her sister Mary wasn't pitching in. Jesus slowed her down: "Martha, Martha, . . . you are worried and upset about many things, but . . . Mary has chosen what is better" (Luke 10:41–42). He says the same to a million Marthas today: Throw away a few of those extraneous "things" and focus on me. I will bring some order to your confusing life.

Instructions:

BEGINNING in Week 5 of the Adventure, look at the "clutter" in your life. This can come in many forms.

● **Space Clutter.** What we usually mean by "clutter." Junk in your living or working space.

● **Schedule Clutter.** Too many things to do and never enough time.

● **Input Clutter.** Too many things to read, TV shows to watch, CDs to listen to.

● **Responsibility Clutter.** Too many responsibilities, not enough delegation.

● **Emotional Clutter.** Too many worries. Grudges held. Blaming yourself for things needlessly.

● **Spiritual Clutter.** Misconceptions that affect your relationship with God. "Idols." Habitual sins.

Choose one specific thing you can do to remove a bit of clutter from your life. Give up an activity. Cancel a subscription. Forgive an age-old offense. Ask God's forgiveness. Hold a yard sale. Whatever. You choose from the specifics of your life. Don't say, "I'll be more available to my kids." Be specific and say, "I will quit the Textbook Committee and spend that time at home."

Once you've selected the clutter to remove and how to do it—do it. Choose a second thing and do it. Now choose a third thing and do it.

There, you've cut out some of the unnecessary confusion. And you don't need to stop with three. Reminders throughout the journal will help you track your progress.

ACTION STEP SUMMARY

READ THIS SUMMARY to get acquainted with the Adventure and to see how often the various action steps are to be done. (For a full description of the action steps, see pp. 7–11.) Remember: This journal will give you daily reminders and weekly checkups to guide you through the assignments.

DAILY
Action Step 1
Fill Your Days with "I Believe" Statements
Pray the "I Believe" Prayer using the model on page 7.
Say "I believe" statements throughout each day.

Action Step 2
Face Confusion with Confidence from God's Word
Study the assigned Scripture passages and answer the questions in the journal each day. Don't forget to seriously consider the optional suggestions (p. 8).

Action Step 4
Energize Your Faith by Tracking Daily Joys
Each day look for a joy and write it down in the Daily Joy Tracker on pages 40–41. Every Wednesday give joy to someone else.

WEEKLY
Read the appropriate chapter in *When Life Becomes a Maze: Discovering Christ's Resources for Times of Confusion* by David Mains (see p. 19).

THREE TIMES DURING THE ADVENTURE
Action Step 5
Find Three Ways to Unclutter Your Life
Beginning in Week 5, choose three specific ways to remove clutter from your life, and try more if necessary.

FOUR TIMES DURING THE ADVENTURE
Action Step 3
Unleash the Power of Prayer Partnerships
Find prayer partners and meet together for at least four half-hour sessions during the Adventure. Use the guidelines on pages 34–35.

■■■■■■■■·■■■■■■■·■■■■■■■·■■■■■■■·■■■■■■■·■■■■■■■·■■■■■■·■

ADVENTURING WITH FAMILY AND FRIENDS

Options for Adults

MANY PEOPLE find it extremely beneficial to have an accountability relationship with another adult who is participating in the Adventure. This might be a prayer partner, a friend, a spouse, or another adult member of your family.

The simplest way to work with someone else is to complete the daily journal entries on your own, then occasionally meet together in person or over the phone to share insights and check on each other's progress.

Married couples, prayer partners, college roommates, and adult singles might choose a more in-depth approach. A daily or weekly fellowship time can be guided by discussing the Adventure action steps and the questions for each day in the journal.

Action Step 3, "Unleash the Power of Prayer Partnerships," provides a built-in way to share your Adventure experience with someone. Here are other ideas you might use:

● Get together at the end of each week and talk about that week's topic and what you've learned. Take turns reading the related Scripture passages you've studied.

● Plan a get-together with other adult Christians to discuss the Adventure action steps. Share some of the joys you've tracked and offer each other ideas for uncluttering your lives.

● Ask another Christian to watch the "You Need to Know" Adventure television programs and discuss them with you.

● Invite a friend to join you in reading *When Life Becomes a Maze* by David Mains (or listen to the audiobook). Discuss a chapter or two each time you meet.

Journals for the Entire Family

AS A HELP to families, we've created four different age-graded journals. They allow both adults and children to work through the same basic Adventure themes, scriptures, and assignments at the same time.

In addition to the Adult Journal, we have a Student Journal for junior- and senior-high schoolers, a Children's Journal for grades 3–6, and an Activity Book for children in kindergarten—grade 2.

Some parents like to go over the materials with their children on a daily basis. If you have younger children, this is actually a necessity. With this age-group, the Adventure activities often fit in nicely at breakfast or bedtime.

Older children may want to complete their journal after school so you can discuss over dinner what you're both learning.

Families with teens might want to schedule a weekly discussion over Friday night pizza. Some parents and teens work on their journals together, but most complete their journals on their own.

Your family situation is unique. Feel free to adapt the Adventure to meet your needs.

More Help for Using Journals with Your Family

DURING THE ADVENTURE adults will focus on eight ways to deal with confusion and place their trust in Christ. These eight topics have been adjusted to meet the special needs of each age-group (see below).

● **Parents of Teens:** The topics for adults and youth are identical, though the wording in the Student Journal has been slanted to the specific needs of junior-high and high-school students.

Because the basic ideas, action steps, and Scripture assignments are the same, you can use this Adventure as an opportunity to get to know the spiritual side of your young adult. Ask for your son or daughter's opinion on the Scripture passages or for input on one of the questions in your journal. Teens may not feel comfortable sharing everything in their journal, but you can use the Adventure as an opportunity to open up discussion.

● **Parents of Children in Grades 3—6:** Your older grade-school children can probably complete the journal on their own. However, a child of this age enjoys the daily encouragement and affirmation of a parent. Complete your journal, then use what you've discovered to add to what your child is learning. Work together on Scripture memory and action steps (Belief Boosters for kids). Your child will be exploring many of the same Scripture passages that you will study.

● **Parents of Children in Kindergarten—Grade 2:** These little ones will need your active involvement to complete their journals. The Activity Book is designed as a "read to me" journal, though the captions on each page are intended for children to read themselves.

Read the daily material together. Each day's reading includes a question to discuss or an idea for applying the lesson. Also have your child complete the activity provided. Unlike other age-groups, younger children will not complete the five action steps, but your child will be working on Scripture memory each week.

If your church is using the Adventure curriculum for grades 1–6, your child will be given a take-home paper each week with ideas for family discussion.

Adventure Themes (The Same, but Different)

A S A FURTHER HELP to families working together on the Adventure, here is a list of the eight weekly topics addressed in the Adult Journal along with changes we've made for students and children. You can refer to the information that follows in planning a daily or weekly Adventure family time.

As you work through these topics on your own, take time to talk to your child about what he or she is learning about handling confusion. Remember, one of the greatest things you can do for your children is to admit that you are sometimes confused, and that you are willing to talk about their feelings of confusion.

The topics for children and students are similar to the adult topics. Each of the eight topics for children is a piece of Adventure Gear, or a resource, that Jesus provides for mixed-up times. On the following page is a list that shows how the topics for adults, students, and children relate.

Topic 1
Adult: Choose to believe Christ will make a way for you through the maze
Student: Choose to believe Christ is with you in the craziness
Children's Adventure Gear: Jesus' help

Topic 2
Adult: Embrace the great promises of God's Word
Student: Hug the great promises of God's Word
Children's Adventure Gear: Jesus' promises

Topic 3
Adult: Pursue support relationships with other believers
Student: Find friends to lean on
Children's Adventure Gear: Jesus' people

Topic 4
Adult: Look for the joys that refresh your spirit
Student: Look for the good stuff
Children's Adventure Gear: Jesus' joy

Topic 5
Adult: Remove unnecessary confusion from your life
Student: Get rid of clutter in your life
Children's Adventure Gear: Time with Jesus

Topic 6
Adult: Accept the Lord's grace and forgiveness
Student: Be free and clear
Children's Adventure Gear: Jesus' forgiveness

Topic 7
Adult: Discover how Jesus identifies with your struggles
Student: Discover how Jesus understands your struggles
Children's Adventure Gear: Jesus' understanding

Topic 8
Adult: Place your hope in the God of surprising outcomes
Student: Expect God to surprise you
Children's Adventure Gear: Jesus' surprises

Tackling Action Steps Together

IF YOU'RE A PARENT, take time to read through the introduction and action step assignments in your child's journal. Younger children do not have action steps, but related activities are sometimes suggested. For older children the action steps are Backpack Belief Boosters. Although they have different names, most of the activities are the same as yours.

EVERYONE PRAYS DAILY. Adults and youth will both use the same "I Believe" Prayer for Action Step l. Older children will use their own version, the Signal Flare Prayer. Younger children will use a shorter prayer, particularly during Week l.

EVERYONE READS THE BIBLE. Adults and students read a daily Scripture passage and answer questions in the journal. Most of the daily Scripture selections for older children correspond to what adults and students are studying. Older and younger children all memorize the same basic Scripture verses on Saturdays.

EVERYONE DEVELOPS PRAYER RELATIONSHIPS WITH OTHERS. Adults and students will form prayer partnerships, and older children will pray with a "believing buddy." Younger children also will be encouraged to pray with a friend or family member.

EVERYONE LOOKS FOR JOYS. Adults, students, and older children will track the daily joys they see in their life. Younger children will learn to look for hidden joys during Week 4. Families or roommates could also keep a joy jar or box. Use slips of paper to record the joys you experience as a group.

EVERYONE WORKS ON MAKING ROOM FOR GOD. Adults, students, and older children will do this by removing clutter from their lives. Younger children will explore the importance of spending time with Jesus.

A Fun Family Video for Adventure Topic 6
Veggie Tales: God Wants Me to Forgive Them*?!?*
by Big Idea Productions

Your kids will enjoy Bob the tomato and Larry the cucumber in their fully animated adventures. This VHS videotape contains two stories of vegetable characters that teach your children biblical perspectives on forgiveness. First your kids will meet the very cranky Grapes of Wrath who make fun of Jr. Asparagus. Then a three-hour boat ride takes a turn for the worse when first mate Larry crashes into a deserted island. Captain Bob and the others discover the real reasons God wants us to forgive.

Adults and children alike will love the original music, groundbreaking animation, and Christian values of this 30-minute Veggie Tales video.

Request your copy of this resource today. Use the order form on page 80 for convenient home delivery, or ask for the video at your church or local Christian bookstore.

Warm-up *Friday, Date* _____

Read Matthew 2:1—23.

1. Notice the series of events: First Jesus is worshiped by wise men, then the holy family is forced to flee as fugitives. What doubts might this have put in the minds of Mary and Joseph?

_____

_____

_____

_____

2. Through what events did God make a way for Mary and Joseph? What was their response to God's leading?

_____

_____

_____

_____

3. Review the circumstances surrounding Jesus' birth (see Matthew 1:18—25 and Luke 1:26—38). Do you think Mary and Joseph were confused at any point? How did each of them respond?

_____

_____

_____

_____

4. Think of a time when you knew God wanted you to do something specific, but you didn't know how it was going to turn out. What was your response? What can you learn from Mary and Joseph's obedience to help you follow God's promptings in the future?

_____

_____

_____

5. Complete this sentence based on today's reading: *When I don't know what to do, I should . . .*

_____

_____

_____

☐ Read the introductory material on pages 3—12.

☐ Pray the "I Believe" Prayer on page 7.

☐ Read the introduction in *When Life Becomes a Maze* (see p. 19).

● **Warm-up** | *Saturday, Date* _____

Read Job 2:1—10.

1. Skim chapter 1. Describe in your own words what has happened to Job so far. What areas of Job's life were affected by his sufferings?

_____
_____
_____
_____

2. Have you had an experience where you were confused but only later realized that Satan had been attacking you? What was your initial response to the situation? Once Satan's hand was revealed, did you respond differently? How?

_____
_____
_____
_____

3. Notice the advice Job's wife gives him in verse 9. Contrast this with Job's "I believe" statement in Job 13:15 (for more on "I believe" statements see p. 7).

_____
_____
_____
_____

4. How did Job respond to his wife (Job 2:10)? In confusing situations are your responses to God similar to Job's? Why or why not?

_____
_____
_____
_____

5. Like Job, we all experience trouble and confusion at some point. This Adventure is about trusting God when life gets confusing. Read Proverbs 3:5—6. What do these verses say to you as you begin this Adventure?

_____
_____
_____
_____

☐ Read the introductory material on pages 3–12.

☐ Pray the "I Believe" Prayer (see p. 7).

☐ Read the introduction in *When Life Becomes a Maze* (see p. 19).

■■■■■■■·■■■■■■■·■■■■■■■·■■■■■■■·■■■■■■■·■■■■■■■·■■■■■■■·■

LOOKING · BACK ·

Check the box if you have completed the assignment.

☐ Read the introductory material on pages 3–12.

☐ Read the introduction in *When Life Becomes a Maze*.

☐ Completed the warm-up days on pages 17–18.

LOOKING · AHEAD ·

Topic 1: Choose to believe Christ will make a way for you through the maze

Assignment for This Week:
● Read chapter 1 in *When Life Becomes a Maze*.

Daily Assignments:
● Pray the "I Believe" Prayer (see p. 7).
● Make "I believe" statements (see p. 7).
● Read the assigned Scripture passages and answer the questions (see p. 8).
● Track daily joys on pages 40–41 (see p. 10).

A Necessary Resource for This 50-Day Adventure:

When Life Becomes a Maze: Discovering Christ's Resources for Times of Confusion
by David Mains (book or audiobook)

In addition to your journals each household needs one copy of *When Life Becomes a Maze*. This essential easy-to-read guidebook includes a chapter for each of the eight Adventure topics. In it you'll find:
● motivational Adventure insights and inspiration
● practical helps and illustrations
● in-depth Adventure topic explanations
● additional suggestions for completing your action steps.

A Recommended Resource for this Adventure:

Believe It Or Not Scripture Promise Pack
by The Chapel Ministries

This handy pack gives you a way to keep the promises of God's Word at your fingertips everywhere you go. It includes 16 promise scriptures that relate specifically to the Adventure topics. You'll find this pack extremely helpful for completing Action Steps 1 and 2. Use it to fuel your faith as you become an "I Believe" person and embrace the great promises of God's Word.

Request your copies of these resources today. Use the order form on page 80 in this journal for convenient home delivery, or ask for these resources at your church or local Christian bookstore.

Day 1

Introduction to Topic 1:
Choose to believe Christ will make a way for you through the maze

Sunday, Date _____   Topic 1 runs Sunday through Friday, Days 1–6.

Pray

May I live confident that you, Lord, are in control.

Read

Read John 14:1–27.

Reflect

It's easy to follow Christ when everything is unfolding exactly the way we want it to. That's like the disciples who take great delight in Christ's miracles and the crowds that follow him and the obvious kingdom momentum. But in the Gospel narrative, circumstances have changed. Because their Lord is not acting the way they expected him to, doubts and confusion mark the Twelve.

In today's passage, Christ encourages those closest to him to continue to exercise faith. He promises them peace and tells them not to let their hearts be troubled. When confusion marks our faith walk, the natural tendency is to stop believing. This is the exact opposite of what we should do. Even when life is bewildering, we can make the conscious choice to believe that the Lord will make a way for us through the maze.

Which response is most characteristic of you—doubt or faith?

Apply

John 14:1–4 talks about our future with Christ in heaven. Do your times of confusion cause you to forget or neglect the importance of this promise? How can the hope of your future in heaven help put times of confusion in perspective?

_____

_____

Think of an area of confusion in your life. According to verses 25–27, how does the Holy Spirit help to make a way for you through your maze?

_____

_____

In verses 10–12 Jesus challenges Philip to believe. What are some "I believe" statements from today's reading you can bring to your confusion? (For example: I believe Jesus wants to give me peace; I don't need to be troubled or afraid.)

_____

_____

Pray

Pray the "I Believe" Prayer (see p. 7).

DAY 2 *Monday, Date* _____

Read Genesis 45:1—11.

1. List some difficult and confusing situations Joseph faced before this time in his life. (See Genesis 37:5–36; 39:1–23; 41:41–43.) How did Joseph respond to these challenges?

_____

_____

_____

2. Joseph may not have understood God's purpose behind all the events in his life until Genesis 45:7–8. Can you recall a situation where God's plan seemed more apparent to you in hindsight? How does that help you deal with present areas of confusion?

_____

_____

_____

3. Joseph lived faithfully even when he didn't understand God's purpose in allowing bad things to happen to him. What is an area of confusion in your life where you can be faithful even though you don't understand why things are happening the way they are?

_____

_____

_____

4. In Genesis 37:5–10 Joseph receives a promise from God in a dream. Do you think Joseph kept faith in this promise even though his situation got worse and worse? What is a promise from Scripture you can rely on during times of uncertainty? (Consider this week's promise scripture, Romans 8:28.)

_____

_____

5. Make Genesis 45:8 into an "I believe" statement that is appropriate for a confusing situation in your life.

_____

_____

_____

☐ Read the introductory material on pages 3–12.

☐ Pray the "I Believe" Prayer (see p. 7).

☐ Make "I believe" statements (see p. 7).

☐ Track daily joys on pages 40–41 (see p. 10).

☐ Read chapter 1 in *When Life Becomes a Maze* (see p. 19).

Read Psalm 27.

1. What is David's desire in verses 4–6? What does his example indicate about an appropriate response to times of confusion? How does this compare with your response to your own confusing situations?

_____

_____

_____

2. What is the tone of verses 7–12? Do David's pleas contradict his statements of confidence in the beginning of the psalm? Explain your answer.

_____

_____

_____

_____

3. If you were writing your own version of verses 7–12, what personal concerns would you include?

_____

_____

_____

_____

4. David expresses strong confidence that the Lord will provide a way out of his present troubles. What "I believe" statements does David use in this psalm?

_____

_____

_____

_____

5. Which of the above "I believe" statements do you find helpful in your own confusion?

_____

_____

_____

☐ Read the introductory material on pages 3–12.

☐ Pray the "I Believe" Prayer (see p. 7).

☐ Make "I believe" statements (see p. 7).

☐ Track daily joys on pages 40–41.

☐ Read chapter 1 in *When Life Becomes a Maze* (see p. 19).

DAY 4   Wednesday, Date _____

Read Hebrews 11.

1. Pick one of the following characters and read more about him or her.

☐ Noah (Genesis 5:28–9:29)

☐ Abraham (Genesis 12:1–7 or 17:15–22 & 21:1–7 or 22:1–19)

☐ Moses (Exodus 1:22–2:25 & 12:1–42)

☐ Rahab (Joshua 2)

Describe the confusion the person faced. What was the key to getting through the situation?

_____

_____

_____

2. What can this person's life teach you about dealing with your confusion?

_____

_____

3. According to Hebrews 11:6 how important is faith? How can you become more faith-centered when you are confused?

_____

_____

_____

4. The discussion of faith in this chapter follows directly from Hebrews 10:38–39. Think of an area of confusion in your life. In what ways might you be tempted to "shrink back"? How does today's passage help you believe and keep going?

_____

_____

_____

5. Who is one person you know who could be included in a modern-day Hebrews 11? What can you learn from this "I believe" person?

_____

_____

☐ Read the introductory material on pages 3–12.

☐ Pray the "I Believe" Prayer (see p. 7).

☐ Make "I believe" statements (see p. 7).

☐ Give joy to someone (record this on pp. 40–41).

☐ Read chapter 1 in *When Life Becomes a Maze* (see p. 19).

Read Isaiah 40:27—31.

1. These verses appear after Isaiah has announced Israel's coming judgment and captivity. He comforts the southern kingdom by reminding them of God's care. In light of their coming punishment how do you think the people responded to this message of hope?

_____
_____
_____

2. According to verse 27 Israel thinks God has forgotten them. Have you ever had similar feelings? Explain.

_____
_____
_____

3. What qualities of the Lord does Isaiah highlight to comfort Israel? Which one of these qualities speaks most to your situation? Why?

_____
_____
_____

4. What is the chief quality of those who will be renewed by God (verse 31)? Just a few days into the Adventure, have you grown in hope in the midst of your confusion? How?

_____
_____
_____

5. Do you think Israel appreciated these verses during their captivity? What does this say about how adversity should affect our relationship with God? How can you better appreciate God's concern for you in your present situation?

_____
_____
_____
_____

☐ Pray the "I Believe" Prayer (see p. 7).

☐ Make "I believe" statements.

☐ Track daily joys on pages 40—41.

☐ Read chapter 1 in *When Life Becomes a Maze* (see p. 19).

TODAY'S PROMISE   **Romans 8:28**

Read Romans 8:26—39.

1. What is the main point of this passage?

_____
_____
_____

2. In verse 32 Paul reasons that if God gave up his Son for us, he will certainly provide us with important blessings and provisions. Does this argument give you confidence that God will provide for your needs in times of confusion? How?

_____
_____
_____

3. How does your present situation compare with the list in verses 38—39? Repeat these verses, inserting your own specific difficulty in the appropriate place.

_____
_____
_____

4. List some of the "I believe" statements you find in Romans 8. (Hint: You can make statements out of questions.)

_____
_____
_____
_____

5. Which of these statements do you believe are true for you right now?

_____
_____
_____
_____

☐ Pray the "I Believe" Prayer (see p. 7).

☐ Make "I believe" statements.

☐ Track daily joys on pages 40—41.

☐ Read chapter 1 in *When Life Becomes a Maze* (see p. 19).

LOOKING · BACK ·

Check the box if you have completed the assignment.

☐ Completed Days 1–6.

☐ Prayed the "I Believe" Prayer.

☐ Made "I believe" statements.

☐ Tracked daily joys.

☐ Read chapter 1 in *When Life Becomes a Maze* (see p. 19).

Optional Follow-up Scriptures for Extra Study on Topic 1:
Ephesians 3:14–21
Isaiah 43:1–2
Psalm 34
Psalm 91

LOOKING · AHEAD ·

Topic 2: Embrace the great promises of God's Word

Assignments for This Week:
● Read chapter 2 in *When Life Becomes a Maze*.
● Read pages 34–35 and find prayer partners for Action Step 3.

Daily Assignments:
● Pray the "I Believe" Prayer (see p. 7).
● Make "I believe" statements.
● Read the assigned Scripture passages and answer the questions.
● Track daily joys on pages 40–41.

An Optional Resource for Adventure Topic 2:
Don't Die in the Winter: Your Season Is Coming
by Dr. Millicent Thompson

When our lives seem overwhelming, it's critical that we learn to trust Christ and embrace the great promises of God's Word. Why? God uses the bitter, lonely, cold winter seasons of our lives to develop Christlike character in us. Reading *Don't Die in the Winter* will help you prepare for the adversity of your winters by discovering God's promises of the blessings of spring.

Request your copy today. Use the order form on page 80 in this journal for convenient home delivery, or ask for this resource at your church or local Christian bookstore.

Saturday/Sunday, Dates _____   Topic 2 runs Saturday through Friday, Days 7–13.

Pray

In difficult times, Lord, I choose to believe that you want to prove to me the truth of your promises.

Read

Read Matthew 4:1–11.

Reflect

No soldier would go on patrol without a weapon. That's like asking for trouble.

Christians don't always know when the enemy will appear. But attacks are a certainty, especially if Satan senses any signs of weakness.

How important it is to be armed with God's truth, to have appropriate promises from God's Word instantly available. Isn't this what Christ models for us here? How interesting that after a brief skirmish the devil chooses to leave. Apparently, the Sword of the Spirit has taken its toll on him!

At a time of weakness, what might Satan whisper in your ear? And what passage can you immediately bring up to counterattack? Such face-offs are usually won or lost quite quickly. The factor which determines the outcome is how skilled the person is at using the Word as an offensive weapon.

With this in mind, what verse do you need handy for the immediate future?

Apply

What kinds of temptations do you need to be on your guard against?

_____

_____

How can relying on Scripture during those times provide strength for you?

_____

_____

Do you know enough Scripture to effectively combat temptation?

_____

_____

How might Jesus' example encourage you to learn more about Scripture?

_____

_____

Pray

Pray the "I Believe" Prayer (see p. 7).

● DAY 9 | *Monday, Date* _____

Read Psalm 19:7—14.

l. Notice the qualities David ascribes to God's Word in verses 7–ll. Have these qualities proved true in your life? Explain.

_____

_____

_____

2. David faced many times of confusion in his life. (See l Samuel 19 for one example.) Yet he found comfort and strength in the promises God had given him. When have you drawn comfort from the promises in God's Word?

_____

_____

_____

3. Which most characterizes David's view of Scripture: a set of harsh rules, or words to rejoice in? Which best reflects your perception? What changes would you like to see in your approach to Scripture?

_____

_____

_____

4. In times of confusion one thing we can do is obey what God has shown us to do through his Word. What is one specific way you can follow the directions of God's Word today? How might that help minimize your confusion?

_____

_____

_____

5. Review verses 7–ll. Choose an "I believe" statement from these verses that reminds you of the truth of God's Word in your area of confusion.

_____

_____

_____

_____

☐ Pray the "I Believe" Prayer (see p. 7).

☐ Make "I believe" statements.

☐ Track daily joys on pages 40–41.

☐ Pray about finding prayer partners (see p. 9).

☐ Read chapter 2 in *When Life Becomes a Maze* (see p. 19).

Read 2 Peter 1:3—4.

1. According to these verses what has God given us?

_____

_____

2. What is the purpose of God's promises for us? How does that affect the way you view the role of God's promises in your life?

_____

_____

3. How does knowing you have been given everything you need for life and godliness change your perspective on your situation?

_____

_____

4. What is one promise from this Adventure that has helped you become an "I believe" person? How has it helped you to trust Christ in areas of confusion?

_____

_____

☐ Pray the "I Believe" Prayer (see p. 7).

☐ Make "I believe" statements.

☐ Track daily joys on pages 40—41.

☐ Pray about finding prayer partners (see p. 9).

☐ Read chapter 2 in *When Life Becomes a Maze* (see p. 19).

STU DAWSON FOUND THAT OFFERING A LITTLE INCENTIVE GREATLY INCREASED THE ENTHUSIASM FOR THE FAMILY'S NIGHTLY DEVOTIONS.

Read Joshua 21:43—45.

1. This passage shows the fulfillment of God's promise to Abraham several hundred years earlier (Genesis 17:7–8). God's timetable often differs from human timetables. When has that been true in your life?

_____

_____

_____

2. When the Israelites first explored the land God had promised them, they were confused because the obstacles seemed so great (see Numbers 13:1–2, 26–33). Yet Joshua 21:45 says all of God's promises to Israel were fulfilled. Does this example of God's faithfulness encourage you to embrace the promises in God's Word? Why or why not?

_____

_____

_____

_____

3. Is there a modern-day situation you know of where God's victory first seemed impossible but was completed in time? What effect does this example have on your attitude toward your confusion?

_____

_____

_____

_____

4. Are there promises God has given us in his Word that are hard to believe? Explain. What "I believe" statement can you make to affirm God's faithfulness?

_____

_____

_____

_____

☐ Pray the "I Believe" Prayer (see p. 7).

☐ Make "I believe" statements.

☐ Give joy to someone (record this on pp. 40—41).

☐ Find prayer partners and plan meetings (see guidelines on p. 34).

☐ Read chapter 2 in *When Life Becomes a Maze* (see p. 19).

Read Psalm 145.

. List some of the things for which David is praising the Lord. If you were writing a similar psalm, what are some phrases you would use to praise God?

_____

_____

_____

. What is the tone of this passage? How could praying through this psalm help give you perspective during times of confusion?

_____

_____

_____

. In verse 13 David writes, "The Lord is faithful to all his promises." How does this statement impact the way you view God's promises?

_____

_____

_____

_____

. What is one promise from Scripture you often think about? Reread the last part of verse 13 and insert your promise at the end as a specific example of David's statement.

The Lord is faithful to all his promises and loving toward all he has made. He . . .

_____

_____

_____

_____

. Do you find it difficult or easy to take God at his word regarding this promise (or somewhere in between)? Explain.

_____

_____

_____

_____

☐ Pray the "I Believe" Prayer (see p. 7).

☐ Make "I believe" statements.

☐ Track daily joys on pages 40–41.

☐ Plan your first prayer partner meeting (see p. 34).

☐ Read chapter 2 in *When Life Becomes a Maze* (see p. 19).

● DAY 13 | *Friday, Date* _____

 **Philippians 1:6**

Read Philippians 1:3—6.

1. What about the Philippian believers is Paul thankful for? Since Paul wrote this letter in prison, what do his words show about his focus during trying times?

_____
_____
_____

2. Notice in verse 6 that God's work takes place "in you." Does it comfort you to know that God is working within you no matter what is happening around you? How?

_____
_____
_____

3. The "good work" Paul is describing is the process of spiritual growth. What are some typical signs of spiritual growth?

_____
_____
_____

4. What evidence do you have that God might be working in you in your present circumstances? How might this remind you to look for signs of the Lord's work during confusing times?

_____
_____
_____

5. Pick one area of confusion in your life. What confidence can you gain by embracing the promises in God's Word? As you study Scripture each day during the Adventure, be on the lookout for specific promises that encourage you in times of confusion.

_____
_____

☐ Pray the "I Believe" Prayer (see p. 7).

☐ Make "I believe" statements.

☐ Track daily joys on pages 40–41.

☐ Sign the Prayer Partner Covenant (p. 35) and plan to meet with prayer partners.

☐ Read chapter 2 in *When Life Becomes a Maze* (see p. 19).

LOOKING · BACK ·

Check the box if you have completed the assignment.

☐ Completed Days 7–13.

☐ Prayed the "I Believe" Prayer.

☐ Made "I believe" statements.

☐ Tracked daily joys.

☐ Read chapter 2 in *When Life Becomes a Maze.*

☐ Read pages 34–35 and found prayer partners for Action Step 3.

Optional Follow-up Scriptures for Extra Study on Topic 2:

I Corinthians 10:13
Ephesians 6:10–18
Deuteronomy 7:9
Psalm 119:105

LOOKING · AHEAD ·

Topic 3: Pursue support relationships with other believers

Assignments for This Week:

● Read chapter 3 in *When Life Becomes a Maze.*
● Meet with your prayer partners for Action Step 3.

Daily Assignments:

● Pray the "I Believe" Prayer.
● Make "I believe" statements.
● Read the assigned Scripture passages and answer the questions.
● Track daily joys on pages 40–41.

An Optional Resource for Adventure Topic 3:

Two Are Better than One: A Guide to Prayer Partnerships That Work
by David Mains and Steve Bell

Simple and potent—that's what prayer partnerships are. This step-by-step guide provides inspiration and practical help for anyone wishing to pursue support relationships with other believers. In this book you'll find:

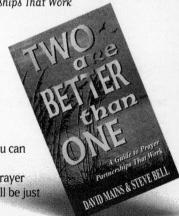

● instructional stories and illustrations
● worksheets and prayer logs
● more than 125 Scripture praises and promises you can use in your prayer time

If you long to energize your spiritual life through prayer partnerships, the proven principles in this book will be just what you're looking for.

Request your copy today. Use the order form on page 80 in this journal for convenient home delivery, or ask for this resource at your church or local Christian bookstore.

● ACTION STEP 3   *Unleash the Power of Prayer Partnerships*

(See p. 9 for a complete description of Action Step 3.)

Session 1
1. Read aloud and sign the Prayer Partner Covenant on page 35.
2. Ask each other, "In what areas of your life do you find confusion?" Consider areas such as health, relationships, work, important decisions, times of discouragement, and so on. Listen carefully but resist the temptation to "solve" your partners' dilemmas.
3. Pray together, asking the Lord to help you and your partner(s) deal with your confusions. Keep notes so you can see how God answers your prayers.

Session 2
1. Reread the covenant on page 35. Have you abided by it?
2. Review the areas of confusion you prayed about last time. Have these situations become more confusing or less confusing, or have they stayed about the same? How does God seem to be answering your prayers?
3. Are there any new areas of confusion? Focus especially on any spiritual concerns you may have related to confusion. Ask each other, "How are you doing right now spiritually? How can I encourage you in prayer?"
4. Take notes and pray together about your spiritual walk with God as well as any other confusing areas of life.

Session 3
1. Review the areas of confusion you have mentioned before. How are you doing with these? Discuss decisions you might make, the options available, or things you'd like to see happen.
2. Think back to a time a year ago or more when you were confused about something that has since been resolved. What happened with that? How did you get through it? What decisions did you make? Tell each other your stories.
3. Discuss any new areas of confusion. Consider especially possible areas of confusion your church may be experiencing, such as leadership changes, tragic events, and so on.
4. Pray with each other about your personal confusions, your spiritual growth, and your hopes for your church.

Session 4
1. Review the areas of confusion shared in past sessions. How has God been answering your prayers?
2. Have you gained any new insight in any of these areas? If you want, you might ask each other for an opinion or advice regarding one of these areas. If you are asked, offer your perspective in a nonjudging way.
3. Discuss ways you might unclutter your life (see Action Step 5 on p. 11).
4. Pray together.
5. Talk about whether you might continue this prayer partnership after the Adventure is over. Even if you don't meet together, you could check in with each other and offer support in the days ahead.

PRAYER PARTNER COVENANT

We are joining in a prayer partnership for the 50-Day Spiritual Adventure.

We agree to:

- Meet at least four times during the Adventure.

- Withhold judgment on problems or doubts shared by partner(s). Our attitude will be one of acceptance.

- Avoid the temptation to try to solve each other's problems during these sessions. Our purpose for meeting is primarily to pray.

- Keep everything at these meetings completely confidential. We must be able to trust each other if we are to share openly.

Signed,

_____

_____

_____

Saturday/Sunday, Dates _____   Topic 3 runs Saturday through Friday, Days 14–20.

Pray

Lord, sometimes you seem distant from me. Please teach me how to experience your presence more fully.

Read

Read Matthew 18:19–20.

Reflect

A simple secret about praying is that it's easier to do with someone else than it is to do on your own. It's often the case as well that when we pray in groups of two or three, the presence of the Lord is more quickly sensed.

Sometimes Christians get together with the intention of praying, but they spend most of their time discussing their needs or problems. This is a mistake. It's usually not until friends actually come together in his Name and talk to him that the Living Lord makes himself known to them.

Even mature believers sometimes struggle in their private prayer lives. This is especially true during times of stress or confusion. But many will testify that praying with good friends is what brought them through the bleak days.

This is a simple secret that not enough believers have discovered first-hand. What about you?

Apply

Are you likely to go to others for prayer support? Why or why not?

_____

What is an area in your life where another's perspective or feedback could help you?

_____
_____

How do Jesus' words encourage you to experience the power of prayer partnerships for yourself?

_____

What are some ways you can make sure Christ is the focus of your time together?

_____

Pray

Pray the "I Believe" Prayer (see p. 7).

DAY 16

Read 1 Samuel 23:14—18.

1. God had chosen David to be the next king of Israel, yet Saul was still in power. How did God protect David during this confusing time?

_____

_____

_____

_____

2. Why did Jonathan go out to meet David? How did he help David find strength in God?

_____

_____

_____

_____

3. Jonathan encouraged David to remember God's faithfulness. How can you remind others of the promises God has for them in his Word?

_____

_____

_____

_____

4. During this time of extreme testing David found encouragement and support in Jonathan. Has someone recently encouraged you? What is one step you can take to develop a support relationship?

_____

_____

_____

_____

5. Jonathan was the son of Saul, yet he aligned himself with David. What does that say about Jonathan's character? What can you learn from him as you seek to support others?

_____

_____

_____

_____

☐ Pray the "I Believe" Prayer (see p. 7).

☐ Make "I believe" statements.

☐ Track daily joys on pages 40–41.

☐ Meet with prayer partners this week (see Session 1 on p. 34).

☐ Read chapter 3 in *When Life Becomes a Maze.*

Proverbs 17:17; 18:24; 27:9—10, 17.

l. Read Proverbs 17:17. What is the message of this proverb? How does David and Jonathan's friendship in 1 Samuel 23 (see yesterday's passage) illustrate this verse?

_____

_____

_____

2. Read Proverbs 18:24. What does this say about how you should choose your friends? According to this proverb what is the value of pursuing strong support relationships?

_____

_____

_____

3. Read Proverbs 27:9—10. How has the counsel of a friend been important to you recently? Have you been able to help another in this fashion?

_____

_____

_____

4. Notice that verse 10 suggests there are times when friends are more accessible than family. When has this been true in your life? How might you be able to help your friends when they are in need?

_____

_____

_____

5. Read Proverbs 27:17. Name three people who have helped you mature in your Christian walk. What qualities did they possess that enabled them to do this for you? Which of these qualities would you like to develop in order to help others?

_____

_____

_____

☐ Pray the "I Believe" Prayer (see p. 7).

☐ Make "I believe" statements.

☐ Track daily joys on pages 40—41.

☐ Meet with prayer partners this week (see Session 1 on p. 34).

☐ Read chapter 3 in *When Life Becomes a Maze.*

DAY 18 *Wednesday, Date* _____

Read Ecclesiastes 4:9—12.

1. List the reasons the author considers two better than one.

_____
_____
_____
_____

2. From your own life, think of examples where another has helped you get by. Now write your own version of these verses. *Two are better than one, because . . .*

_____
_____
_____
_____
_____

3. What can someone else do to help you through a confusing situation you're in now? Who could provide that support for you? What steps can you take to ask for this help?

_____
_____
_____
_____

4. Who is a person you may be able to provide support for? What specifically could you do to help that person through a confusing situation?

_____
_____
_____
_____

5. How do these verses speak to you as you unleash the power of prayer partnerships?

_____
_____
_____
_____
_____

☐ Pray the "I Believe" Prayer (see p. 7).

☐ Make "I believe" statements.

☐ Give joy to someone (record this on pp. 40–41).

☐ Meet with prayer partners this week (see Session 1 on p. 34).

☐ Read chapter 3 in *When Life Becomes a Maze*.

DAILY JOY TRA

For more information on tracking your daily joys, see page 10.
(Remember to record a joy you give to others on Wednesdays.)

DAY 1 _____

DAY 2 _____

DAY 3 _____

WED., DAY 4 _____

DAY 5 _____

DAY 6 _____

DAY 7 _____

DAY 8 _____

DAY 9 _____

DAY 10 _____

WED., DAY 11 _____

DAY 12 _____

DAY 13 _____

DAY 14 _____

DAY 15 _____

DAY 16 _____

DAY 17 _____

WED., DAY 18 _____

DAY 19 _____

DAY 20 _____

DAY 21 _____

DAY 22 _____

DAY 23 _____

DAY 24 _____

WED., DAY 25 _____

DAY 26 _____

DAY 27_____

DAY 28 _____

DAY 29 _____

DAY 30_____

DAY 31 _____

WED., DAY 32 _____

DAY 33_____

DAY 34 _____

DAY 35_____

DAY 36 _____

DAY 37_____

DAY 38 _____

WED., DAY 39_____

DAY 40_____

DAY 41 _____

DAY 42 _____

DAY 43 _____

DAY 44 _____

DAY 45 _____

WED., DAY 46 _____

DAY 47 _____

DAY 48_____

DAY 49 _____

DAY 50_____

● **DAY 19** *Thursday, Date* _____

Read Galatians 6:2.

I. The early Christians certainly relied on each other in challenging situations. In your confusing times do you tend more to withdraw and try to handle everything on your own, or actively seek support and prayer from other believers? In light of today's readings do you think you need to make any changes? Explain.

_____

_____

_____

_____

2. What does this verse say about Paul's view of support relationships?

_____

_____

_____

3. How have others helped bear your burdens? What is a practical way you can do that for someone else?

_____

_____

_____

4. Read Luke 10:1–3. What example is Jesus setting here? Why do you think he sends the disciples out in twos?

_____

_____

_____

_____

5. The practice of sending believers out in twos was continued in the early church (see Acts 13:2; 15:27, 39–40). Why is it important to team up with others to do God's work?

_____

_____

_____

_____

☐ Pray the "I Believe" Prayer (see p. 7).

☐ Make "I believe" statements.

☐ Track daily joys on pages 40–41.

☐ Meet with prayer partners this week (see Session I on p. 34).

☐ Read chapter 3 in *When Life Becomes a Maze*.

·TODAY'S· PROMISE   **Hebrews 10:23**

Read Hebrews 10:19—25.

1. What is the author asking the Hebrews to do in these verses? What does this passage say about the role of community in helping us "hold unswervingly to the hope we profess"?

_____

_____

_____

2. Some of the Hebrews were being tempted to give up Christianity. What specific advice does the author give them in verses 24–25?

_____

_____

_____

3. What might these verses say to you during confusing times when your faith is being tested?

_____

_____

_____

4. How can you implement the advice of this passage in your prayer partnership for Action Step 3?

_____

_____

_____

5. In what specific ways does the promise of verse 23 speak to your current situation?

_____

_____

_____

☐ Pray the "I Believe" Prayer (see p. 7).

☐ Make "I believe" statements.

☐ Track daily joys on pages 40—41.

☐ Meet with prayer partners this week (see Session 1 on p. 34).

☐ Read chapter 3 in *When Life Becomes a Maze.*

▼

LOOKING · BACK ·

LOOKING · AHEAD ·

Check the box if you have completed the assignment.

☐ Completed Days 14–20.

☐ Prayed the "I Believe" Prayer.

☐ Made "I believe" statements.

☐ Tracked daily joys.

☐ Read chapter 3 in *When Life Becomes a Maze.*

☐ Met with prayer partners.

Optional Follow-up Scriptures for Extra Study on Topic 3:
James 5:13–16
Acts 1:12–14
Acts 2:42–47
Hebrews 3:12–14

Topic 4: Look for the joys that refresh your spirit

Assignments for This Week:
● Read chapter 4 in *When Life Becomes a Maze.*
● Meet with your prayer partners for Action Step 3.
● Begin thinking of ways to unclutter your life for Action Step 5.

Daily Assignments:
● Pray the "I Believe" Prayer.
● Make "I believe" statements.
● Read the assigned Scripture passages and answer the questions.
● Track daily joys on pages 40–41.

An Optional Resource for Adventure Topic 4:
When God Whispers: Glimpses of an Extraordinary God by an Ordinary Woman
by Carole Mayhall

When you look for the joys that refresh your spirit, you often find God speaking in the ordinary, the mundane, the routine of daily life. That's what *When God Whispers* is about: everyday events. It's a book about the refreshing whispers of God. Whispers of love and joy. Grounded in Scripture, this collection of reflections is full of personal experience and insightful meditations that will encourage you to look and listen for God's still, small voice.

Request your copy today. Use the order form on page 80 in this journal for convenient home delivery, or ask for this resource at your church or local Christian bookstore.

Days 21/22 Introduction to Topic 4: Look for the joys that refresh your spirit

Saturday/Sunday, Dates _____   Topic 4 runs Saturday through Friday, Days 21–27.

 Pray   Lord, thank you for providing refreshing stops during long and difficult journeys.

 Read   Read Mark 14:1–11.

Reflect   People caught in the midst of confusion have one great desire. They want their problems resolved as quickly as possible. Sometimes such individuals are so singularly focused they can't see anything else that's happening. But the truth is that problems of magnitude usually take a while to work through, and it's not necessary that life remain joyless until then.

What a great example Christ sets for us in this passage. Though carrying the weight of the world on his shoulders, our Lord doesn't allow what he knows is just ahead to rob him of the tenderness of this special moment. Instead, he receives with joy the love and concern of this nameless woman.

"Why are you bothering her?" Jesus questions his Twelve, who are concerned with the extravagance of the act. "She has done a beautiful thing to me."

When your days are overcast, a good lesson to learn is to look for joys which refresh your spirit. Mastering this skill makes every 24 hours a special adventure with the Lord.

 Apply   What are two ways you can be more sensitive to the joys God gives you?

_____

_____

How can recognizing these joys provide encouragement in confusing situations?

_____

Has practicing Action Step 4 been a help to you? How?

_____

 Pray   Pray the "I Believe" Prayer (see p. 7).

Read 2 Corinthians 6:3—10.

1. Have any of the hardships which Paul describes characterized a confusing time in your life? In situations like these are you able to turn yourself over to God, confident that he will encourage you? Why or why not?

_____
_____
_____
_____

2. Read Acts 16:22–25. What added meaning does this passage give to 2 Corinthians 6:3–10? Does Paul's example of continually finding joy inspire you? How?

_____
_____
_____

3. Who is a person you know who is able to find joy during life's troubles? Is there someone you know who is always looking at the negative? What is one thing you can do to become a commendable example instead of a stumbling block to others?

_____
_____
_____
_____

4. Verse 10 in *The Message* reads, "immersed in tears, yet always filled with deep joy." This passage shows that Paul did not deny his emotional anguish. What does that show about the importance of acknowledging feelings of sorrow while looking for joys?

_____
_____
_____
_____

☐ Pray the "I Believe" Prayer (see p. 7).

☐ Make "I believe" statements.

☐ Track daily joys on pages 40–41.

☐ Plan your second prayer partner meeting (see p. 34).

☐ Think of ways to unclutter your life (see p. 11).

☐ Read chapter 4 in *When Life Becomes a Maze*.

● DAY 24   *Tuesday, Date* _____

Read Philippians 4:4—19.

1. Flip back to Philippians 1:13–14. How does knowing that Paul was writing from prison affect the way you read today's passage?

_____

_____

_____

2. In Philippians 4:4 Paul commands us to rejoice. Does this surprise you considering the trials Paul went through? Would you be so bold if you were in Paul's place? Explain.

_____

_____

_____

3. What is one modern-day example of each of the following:
    something true _____
    something noble _____
    something right _____
    something pure _____
    something lovely _____
    something admirable _____
    something excellent or praiseworthy _____

4. How can concentrating on your answers for question 3 help you "rejoice in the Lord always"—even in confusing times? Be specific.

_____

_____

5. What is the promise (verses 7 and 9) connected with Paul's commands? Is this something you need in your situation? What is one way you can put this passage into practice today?

_____

_____

☐ Pray the "I Believe" Prayer (see p. 7).

☐ Make "I believe" statements.

☐ Track daily joys on pages 40–41.

☐ Meet with prayer partners this week (Session 2).

☐ Think of ways to unclutter your life (see p. 11).

☐ Read chapter 4 in *When Life Becomes a Maze.*

Read 1 Thessalonians 5:16—18.

1. According to these verses what three things are God's will for us?

_____
_____
_____

2. Notice that Paul's three commands are to be carried out continually. Do you find it easier to do these things in times of well-being or in times of difficulty? Why?

_____
_____
_____
_____

3. Think of a confusing situation in which it is hard to put these verses into practice. How do you think things would be different if you could follow Paul's commands?

_____
_____
_____
_____

4. Paul writes that these commands are God's will for us. Even when we don't know what to do about a given situation, here are three things we know to do always. List two or three other things you know to do from God's Word. How might they help you in present areas of confusion?

_____
_____
_____

5. Today for Action Step 4 you are to help bring joy to another person. What can you do to give someone else a reason to be thankful today?

_____
_____
_____

☐ Pray the "I Believe" Prayer (see p. 7).

☐ Make "I believe" statements.

☐ Give joy to someone (record this on pp. 40—41).

☐ Meet with prayer partners this week (Session 2).

☐ Decide on your first "unclutter step" (see p. 11).

☐ Read chapter 4 in *When Life Becomes a Maze*.

Read Ruth 2:1—13.

1. Skim Ruth 1. List some of the things which made this a confusing situation for Ruth and Naomi.

_____

_____

_____

_____

2. Historically Israel and Moab had been bitter enemies. What does this say about Ruth's confession in Ruth 1:16?

_____

_____

_____

3. Though Naomi was a faithful witness for God, she changed her name to Mara (which means bitter) to reflect the afflictions in her life. If you were to change your name to a word which reflects your attitude toward a current area of confusion, what would it be? Why?

_____

_____

_____

4. Review Ruth 2:1—13. If Ruth had been doing Action Step 4, what joys might she have recognized during this confusing time in her life?

_____

_____

_____

5. Read Ruth 4:13—17. Does it encourage you to see the joys God gave Ruth and Naomi through their confusing situation? How?

_____

_____

_____

_____

☐ Pray the "I Believe" Prayer (see p. 7).

☐ Make "I believe" statements.

☐ Track daily joys on pages 40—41.

☐ Meet with prayer partners this week (Session 2).

☐ Decide on your first "unclutter step" (see p. 11).

☐ Read chapter 4 in *When Life Becomes a Maze*.

**·TODAY'S·
PROMISE**   **Lamentations 3:22—23**

Read Lamentations 3:19—23.

1. In Lamentations 1 and 2 Jeremiah mourns over the destruction of Jerusalem. Yet in today's passage he finds hope. What is the basis for his hope?

_____

_____

2. Notice the first phrase in verse 21. What does this indicate about the importance of being intentional in looking for joys in difficult times?

_____

_____

3. How does the promise in verses 22—23 encourage you to look for God's compassions?

_____

_____

4. Take a moment to reflect on verses 22—23. What comfort do these verses give you in your confusion?

_____

_____

_____

_____

5. What difference has tracking joys every day made in your life the last four weeks? Do you feel you are more aware of joys today than you were on Day 1 of the Adventure? What difference has that made in the way you view times of confusion?

_____

_____

_____

_____

☐ Pray the "I Believe" Prayer (see p. 7).

☐ Make "I believe" statements.

☐ Track daily joys on pages 40—41.

☐ Meet with prayer partners this week (Session 2).

☐ Plan your first "unclutter step" (see p. 11).

☐ Read chapter 4 in *When Life Becomes a Maze*.

LOOKING · BACK ·

Check the box if you have completed the assignment.

☐ Completed Days 21–27.

☐ Prayed the "I Believe" Prayer.

☐ Made "I believe" statements.

☐ Tracked daily joys.

☐ Read chapter 4 in *When Life Becomes a Maze*.

☐ Met with prayer partners.

☐ Planned a way to unclutter your life.

Optional Follow-up Scriptures for Extra Study on Topic 4:
Nehemiah 8:1–12
Psalm 4
John 15:9–13
Psalm 70

LOOKING · AHEAD ·

Topic 5: Remove unnecessary confusion from your life

Assignments for This Week:
● Read chapter 5 in *When Life Becomes a Maze*.
● Meet with your prayer partners for Action Step 3.
● Unclutter your life for Action Step 5.

Daily Assignments:
● Pray the "I Believe" Prayer.
● Make "I believe" statements.
● Read the assigned Scripture passages and answer the questions.
● Track daily joys on pages 40–41.

An Optional Resource for Adventure Topic 5:

Margin: Restoring Emotional, Physical, Financial, and Time Reserves to Overloaded Lives
by Richard A. Swenson, M.D.

If you're feeling maxed-out, overstressed, overwhelmed, or overloaded, then you need a strong dose of *Margin*. If you want to remove the unnecessary confusion from your life, then you need to read *Margin*. In this book Dr. Swenson provides a prescription against the danger of overloaded lives. He focuses on four key areas:

● restoring emotional energy   ● finding time
● maintaining physical energy   ● creating financial balance

The result: an uncluttered life that enjoys contentment, simplicity, balance, and rest.

Request your copy today. Use the order form on page 80 in this journal for convenient home delivery, or ask for this resource at your church or local Christian bookstore.

Days 28/29 Introduction to Topic 5: Remove unnecessary confusion from your life

Saturday/Sunday, Dates _____   Topic 5 runs Saturday through Friday, Days 28–34.

Pray

When I face confusion, Jesus, how good it is to be able to see in Scripture how you acted in a similar situation.

Read

Read Mark 1:32–39.

Reflect

Students are given exams in quiet settings. That's because when concentration is required, distractions need to be minimized.

Times of confusion often require quiet seasons of prayer and reflection for a person to be able to process what's going on. The more distractions can be reduced, the better the result.

A full evening of healing the sick and casting out demons probably left Jesus exhausted. He no doubt anticipated longer lines of needy people greeting him the next morning. But was this his primary mission?

Christ got up early so he could spend time with his Father. While praying he realized that his main calling would be diverted if he didn't move on. This was in spite of the fact that his disciples exclaimed, "Everyone is looking for you!"

Removing unnecessary confusion from your life is not always easy, but it's an important lesson in learning to be like Christ.

Apply

Do you feel you have a clear direction for your own life and ministry? What is one step you can take to focus on what God wants from you?

_____

_____

Look at your coming week. What is one way you can eliminate distractions to focus on what is important? How could that help to minimize confusion?

_____

_____

When during the week will you need some time alone to maintain your focus? What can you do now to guard that time?

_____

_____

Pray

Pray the "I Believe" Prayer (see p. 7).

Read Acts 6:1—7.

l. What was the problem? How did the disciples solve the problem?

_____

_____

_____

2. What was the disciples' reasoning for their solution? Notice that their solution neither overlooked the needs of the people nor distracted the disciples from their primary calling.

_____

_____

_____

3. What was the result of the disciples' solution (verse 7)? How might that encourage you to put the principle of delegation into practice?

_____

_____

_____

_____

4. What are responsibilities that are important for you to keep? What are things you do that could be delegated?

_____

_____

_____

5. Action Step 5 of this Adventure is to find three ways to unclutter your life—to remove unnecessary confusion. What ideas do you have about how to do that? (Review Action Step 5, p. ll.)

_____

_____

_____

☐ Pray the "I Believe" Prayer (see p. 7).

☐ Make "I believe" statements.

☐ Track daily joys on pages 40—4l.

☐ Plan your third prayer partner meeting (see p. 34).

☐ Plan your first "unclutter step" (see p. ll).

☐ Read chapter 5 in *When Life Becomes a Maze*.

● **DAY 31** | *Tuesday, Date* _____

Read Exodus 18:13—24.

I. Describe Moses' position of authority and the duty he was performing for the people. How seriously did Moses take his responsibilities of service?

_____

_____

_____

_____

2. What advice did Moses receive from his father-in-law, Jethro? Moses felt an obligation to his people. How would Jethro's suggestions actually help the people more?

_____

_____

_____

_____

3. During times of confusion do you tend to get bogged down with all there is to do? How could delegating help remove unnecessary confusion from your life?

_____

_____

_____

_____

4. Think of a responsibility you need to delegate. How can verse 23 give you courage to follow through on your plan?

_____

_____

_____

_____

☐ Pray the "I Believe" Prayer (see p. 7).

☐ Make "I believe" statements.

☐ Track daily joys on pages 40—41.

☐ Meet with your prayer partners this week (Session 3).

☐ Take your first step in removing clutter from your life.

☐ Read chapter 5 in *When Life Becomes a Maze.*

Read Romans 12:3—8.

1. Why do you think Paul instructs the Romans to have sober judgment about their own gifts and abilities? List some of your strengths and weaknesses.

_____

_____

_____

2. Paul illustrates the importance of understanding one's gifts by using the metaphor of the body. What metaphor would you use today? Is it freeing to know that God has provided others to supplement your strengths and weaknesses? How?

_____

_____

_____

3. Read 1 Corinthians 12:14—20. How does the metaphor of the body impact the way you view your church? Is it necessary to do everything you are asked to do? Why or why not?

_____

_____

_____

4. Have you ever been in a situation where you were doing a task you were not gifted to do? What sort of experience was that for you? How might you better use your gifts to serve God?

_____

_____

_____

5. Paul instructs the Romans to serve others by using their God-given gifts. Today for Action Step 4 you are to bring joy to someone else. Who can you serve by bringing joy to his or her life?

_____

_____

_____

☐ Pray the "I Believe" Prayer (see p. 7).

☐ Make "I believe" statements.

☐ Give joy to someone (record this on pp. 40—41).

☐ Meet with your prayer partners this week (Session 3).

☐ Take your first step in removing clutter from your life.

☐ Read chapter 5 in *When Life Becomes a Maze*.

● **DAY 33**   *Thursday, Date* _____

Read Hebrews 12:1—3.

1. The "great cloud of witnesses" are the heroes of the faith mentioned in chapter 11. According to Hebrews 12:1—3 what is to be our response to their testimony?

_____
_____
_____

2. What are some burdens or sins that hinder you in your spiritual "race"? (See Ephesians 4:25—5:21 for some examples.)

_____
_____
_____

3. What is one burden or sin that you can resolve to "throw off" during this Adventure?

_____
_____
_____

4. What can you do today to fix your eyes on Jesus? How can ridding yourself of burdens or sins help you keep this focus?

_____
_____
_____
_____

5. How do today's passages help you acknowledge the importance of removing unnecessary and burdensome entanglements from your life? How could the instructions in these scriptures be beneficial for you in times of confusion?

_____
_____
_____
_____

☐ Pray the "I Believe" Prayer (see p. 7).

☐ Make "I believe" statements.

☐ Track daily joys on pages 40—41.

☐ Meet with your prayer partners this week (Session 3).

☐ Take your first step in removing clutter from your life.

☐ Read chapter 5 in *When Life Becomes a Maze.*

·TODAY'S· PROMISE ▶   Matthew 6:33

Read Matthew 6:25—34.

1. State Jesus' main point in your own words.

_____
_____
_____

2. What does this passage say about the completeness of God's provision for us? What does it say about what our priority in life should be?

_____
_____
_____

3. What does Jesus indicate about our priorities regarding material provision? Are his instructions easy or difficult to follow in confusing times? Why?

_____
_____
_____

4. Are there some material goals or possessions you have that cause confusion or keep you from focusing on Christ? If so, what?

_____
_____
_____

5. What is one thing you can do to unclutter your life in this area (see Action Step 5 on p. 11)?

_____
_____
_____

☐ Pray the "I Believe" Prayer (see p. 7).

☐ Make "I believe" statements.

☐ Track daily joys on pages 40—41.

☐ Meet with your prayer partners this week (Session 3).

☐ Take your first step in removing clutter from your life.

☐ Read chapter 5 in *When Life Becomes a Maze*.

LOOKING · BACK ·

Check the box if you have completed the assignment.

☐ Completed Days 28–34.

☐ Prayed the "I Believe" Prayer.

☐ Made "I believe" statements.

☐ Tracked daily joys.

☐ Read chapter 5 in *When Life Becomes a Maze*.

☐ Met with prayer partners.

☐ Removed clutter from my life.

Optional Follow-up Scriptures for Extra Study on Topic 5:
Luke 10:38–42
Micah 6:6–8
Matthew 11:28–30
Psalm 131

LOOKING · AHEAD ·

Topic 6: Accept the Lord's grace and forgiveness

Assignments for This Week:
● Read chapter 6 in *When Life Becomes a Maze*.
● Meet with your prayer partners for Action Step 3.
● Unclutter your life for Action Step 5.

Daily Assignments:
● Pray the "I Believe" Prayer.
● Make "I believe" statements.
● Read the assigned Scripture passages and answer the questions.
● Track daily joys on pages 40–41.

An Optional Resource for Adventure Topic 6:
If I'm Forgiven Why Do I Still Feel Guilty?
by Bernard Bangley

Forgiving yourself is often harder than forgiving someone else. If we won't let ourselves off the hook, we probably need to accept the Lord's grace and forgiveness. This encouraging, reader-friendly book will help you:
● distinguish true guilt from false
● explore the nature of God's forgiveness
● resolve guilt through practical suggestions
● deal with conflict between yourself and others

Request your copy today. Use the order form on page 80 in this journal for convenient home delivery, or ask for this resource at your church or local Christian bookstore.

Saturday/Sunday, Dates _____   Topic 6 runs Saturday through Friday, Days 35–41.

Pray

Lord, if I can forgive others when they fail, why should I be slow to accept your gracious forgiveness for my short-comings?

Read

Read Luke 15:11–31.

Reflect

People aren't expected to solve a maze on the first try. By definition, mazes are somewhat confusing.

Maybe you're in a personal maze of your own making. That's the case with the younger son in this passage. He had no one but himself to blame for his problems.

Or perhaps you had little to do with the painful circumstances in which you're ensnared. Either way, life is difficult for you and the path to freedom isn't easy to find.

Times like these are when you need to rest heavily on the Lord's grace and forgiveness. A key lesson in this passage is that the heart of the father is incredibly compassionate and caring. In the same way, our Heavenly Father yearns to take you in his strong arms and demonstrate just how much he cares.

Verse 17 begins, "When he came to his senses." Here was a moment of truth for this young man. For some Christians, coming to their senses could involve understanding that God is more forgiving of what's happened than they are. How amazing!

Apply

How do you feel about going to God when you've made bad choices or experienced hard times?

_____

_____

Sometimes we are afraid to move ahead for fear of making a mistake. How can understanding God's grace help you move forward?

_____

Do you ever feel that God has not forgiven you? Why? What step do you need to take to accept the Lord's forgiveness?

_____

Pray

Pray the "I Believe" Prayer (see p. 7).

DAY 37 *Monday, Date* _____

Read Luke 22:54—62 and John 21:15—19.

I. Review the events which led to Luke 22:54—62. In what ways do you think this was a confusing time for Peter and the rest of the disciples?

_____
_____
_____

2. What does verse 62 show about Peter's feelings toward what he had done?

_____
_____
_____

3. Recall a time when you really blew it with someone or with God. Looking back, how would you handle the situation differently?

_____
_____
_____

4. After his resurrection how did Jesus respond to Peter's denial (John 21:15—19)? Why was this important for Peter? Why is it important that this scene was recorded for us?

_____
_____
_____

5. Notice that in Acts 2:38—39 Peter preaches the forgiveness of sins to his fellow Jews. What does that show about Peter's ability to accept the Lord's forgiveness and move ahead in ministry? In what specific ways can you follow Peter's example?

_____
_____
_____

☐ Pray the "I Believe" Prayer (see p. 7).

☐ Make "I believe" statements.

☐ Track daily joys on pages 40—41.

☐ Plan your fourth prayer partner meeting (see p. 34).

☐ Plan your second "unclutter step" (see p. II).

☐ Read chapter 6 in *When Life Becomes a Maze*.

DAY 38 *Tuesday, Date* _____

Read Philippians 3:12—16.

1. Skim Philippians 3:1–11 for the context of this passage. What is Paul's main point in these verses?

_____
_____
_____
_____

2. Although Paul has not obtained complete perfection, that does not stop his pursuit of it. How do verses 12–16 suggest we deal with past instances which remind us we are not yet perfect?

_____
_____
_____
_____

3. Is Paul's pursuit of the "prize" active or passive? How can you be more active in your walk with God?

_____
_____
_____
_____

4. What is one area of your life you need to "forget" in order to move toward spiritual maturity? How can the principle of forgetting what is behind and straining toward the prize help you when you don't know what to do?

_____
_____
_____
_____

☐ Pray the "I Believe" Prayer (see p. 7).

☐ Make "I believe" statements.

☐ Track daily joys on pages 40–41.

☐ Plan your fourth prayer partner meeting (see p. 34).

☐ Plan your second "unclutter step" (see p. 11).

☐ Read chapter 6 in *When Life Becomes a Maze*.

● **DAY 39** *Wednesday, Date* _____

Read Colossians 3:12—14.

1. Of all the qualities Paul lists in these verses, which are the most challenging for you?

_____

_____

2. This week you have been reading scriptures about God's forgiveness. How have these passages shed light on Paul's instructions to forgive others as God forgave you?

_____

_____

_____

3. Has there been a time when you found it hard to forgive someone? How has that affected other areas of your life?

_____

_____

_____

_____

4. How can forgiving others help you unclutter your life and minimize confusion?

_____

_____

_____

_____

5. Today for Action Step 4 consider giving joy by offering forgiveness to someone who knows you've been nursing a grudge. How can you show forgiveness to this person?

_____

_____

_____

_____

☐ Pray the "I Believe" Prayer (see p. 7).

☐ Make "I believe" statements.

☐ Give joy to someone (record this on pp. 40–41).

☐ Meet with your prayer partners this week (Session 4).

☐ Take your second step in removing clutter from your life.

☐ Read chapter 6 in *When Life Becomes a Maze*.

Read Psalm 51.

1. David had committed adultery and murder, crimes against Israel punishable by death (see 2 Samuel 11:1–12:25). How does this give more meaning to David's words?

_____

_____

2. In Psalm 51:11 David asks that the Holy Spirit not be taken from him. Though the Spirit temporarily empowered Old Testament believers for a specific task, the Holy Spirit permanently indwells Christians. How does it encourage you to know that the Spirit helps you live the way God wants you to?

_____

_____

3. In verses 16–19 David writes about sacrifices and the forgiveness of sin. David's prayers were often accompanied by music. What is a song that reminds you of God's forgiveness through Christ?

_____

_____

4. Think of something for which you need to ask forgiveness. With that in mind, pray verses 1–4 and 10–12 as your prayer to God.

☐ Pray the "I Believe" Prayer (see p. 7).   ☐ Make "I believe" statements.

☐ Track daily joys on pages 40–41.

☐ Meet with your prayer partners this week (Session 4).

☐ Take your second step in removing clutter from your life.

☐ Read chapter 6 in *When Life Becomes a Maze*.

ROGER, WE'VE BEEN OVER THIS BEFORE. I NEED MY CLOSET SPACE. BESIDES, THERE'S MORE ROOM FOR YOUR CLOTHES DOWN HERE.

● **DAY 41** *Friday, Date* _____

·TODAY'S· **PROMISE** ▶ 1 John 1:9

Read 1 John 1:5—10.

1. Reread this passage, replacing the words *we, us,* and *our* with *I, me,* and *my.* What is one way you have seen this passage in a new light by making it more personal?

_____

_____

2. Verse 9 is this week's promise. Do you believe it? Do you believe it on an intellectual level? How about on an emotional level? Explain.

_____

_____

3. Notice that John indicates God cleanses us from "all" unrighteousness. Has there been a time in the past when you felt you were not totally forgiven by God? How does this verse change that perception?

_____

_____

4. Sometimes our confusion is a result of unresolved guilt. Do you have an issue you feel is still unresolved with God at this time? What can you do to accept the Lord's grace and forgiveness?

_____

_____

5. If you have never experienced God's forgiveness and a personal relationship with Christ, who could you talk with to learn more about that (pastor, Christian friend, etc.)?

_____

☐ Pray the "I Believe" Prayer (see p. 7).

☐ Make "I believe" statements.

☐ Track daily joys on pages 40—41.

☐ Meet with your prayer partners this week (Session 4).

☐ Take your second step in removing clutter from your life.

☐ Read chapter 6 in *When Life Becomes a Maze.*

LOOKING · BACK ·

Check the box if you have completed the assignment.

- ☐ Completed Days 35–41.
- ☐ Prayed the "I Believe" Prayer.
- ☐ Made "I believe" statements.
- ☐ Tracked daily joys.
- ☐ Read chapter 6 in *When Life Becomes a Maze*.
- ☐ Met with prayer partners.
- ☐ Removed clutter from my life.

Optional Follow-up Scriptures for Extra Study on Topic 6:
2 Corinthians 5:17–21
Psalm 103
Micah 7:18–20
Titus 3:4–7

LOOKING · AHEAD ·

Topic 7: Discover how Jesus identifies with your struggles
Topic 8: Place your hope in the God of surprising outcomes

Assignments for This Week:
- ● Read chapters 7–8 in *When Life Becomes a Maze*.
- ● Meet with your prayer partners (if you haven't completed four sessions).
- ● Unclutter your life for Action Step 5.

Daily Assignments:
- ● Pray the "I Believe" Prayer.
- ● Make "I believe" statements.
- ● Read the assigned Scripture passages and answer the questions.
- ● Track daily joys on pages 40–41.

An Optional Resource for Adventure Topics 7 and 8:
He Still Moves Stones
by Max Lucado

Renowned Christian author Max Lucado shares real-life stories of the surprises God uses to answer the question "Where is God when I hurt?" *He Still Moves Stones* reminds us that the God who spoke still speaks. The God who forgave still forgives. The God who came still comes. And he comes in surprising ways, to do what we can't. He comes to move the stones we can't budge. He still moves stones.

Request your copy today. Use the order form on page 80 in this journal for convenient home delivery, or ask for this resource at your church or local Christian bookstore.

Days 42/43   Introduction to Topic 7: Discover how Jesus identifies with your struggles

Saturday/Sunday, Dates _____   Topic 7 runs Saturday through Wednesday, Days 42–46.

Pray

Lord, I really want to know just how much you can identify with my struggles.

Read

Read Isaiah 52:13–53:12.

Reflect

When life is confusing, how do you respond when someone says, "I believe I can understand exactly what you're going through"?

"Respond?" you counter. "React would be more precise. I hate it when people say things like that!"

With that typical answer in mind it is best to ease into the Adventure topic we will look at next. Don't react, because it's true that Jesus can identify with your struggles. That fact gives great meaning to our conversations with him about our frustrations and concerns and hurts.

Passages like this need to be read slowly. There need to be pauses for reflection between phrases such as "a man of sorrows" and "familiar with suffering." As you read, decide whether Jesus can rightfully say to you, "I believe I can understand exactly what you're going through."

If your answer is *no*, the week ahead won't be a good one. But if your answer is *yes*, you may discover a wonderful new dimension to your relationship with the Lord.

Apply

According to this passage why was it necessary for Christ to suffer under the weight of sin? How does this impact the way you view his sufferings?

_____

How does it comfort you to know that Christ understands suffering? Does this make you more likely to go to him with your confusion or pain? Why or why not?

_____

How can you respond to God's love today?

_____
_____
_____

Pray

Pray the "I Believe" Prayer (see p. 7).

DAY 44 *Monday, Date* _____

Read Philippians 2:5—11.

1. What do verses 5—8 indicate about Jesus' ability to identify with our struggles? Think of a confusing area of your life. Is it easier to trust Christ knowing that he understands? Why or why not?

_____

_____

_____

2. Verse 7 in *The Message* says Christ "set aside the privileges of deity." Read John 13:12—17. What added appreciation do these verses give you for the servant heart of Jesus?

_____

_____

3. Philippians 2:5—8 says we should imitate Christ's humility and submission. Write down several ways you can be a servant this week. Pick one and do it.

_____

_____

_____

4. Verse 10 says that "at the name of Jesus every knee should bow." Who is someone you know who doesn't recognize Christ as Lord? What is one thing you can do to help this person appreciate Christ's love for him or her?

_____

_____

5. Verses 6—11 were probably from an early Christian hymn. Are you familiar with a hymn or chorus that expresses similar ideas? Remember it throughout the day and let it remind you of Jesus' sufferings for you.

_____

_____

☐ Pray the "I Believe" Prayer (see p. 7).

☐ Make "I believe" statements.

☐ Track daily joys on pages 40—41.

☐ Plan your third "unclutter step" (see p. 11).

☐ Read chapter 7 in *When Life Becomes a Maze.*

Read Hebrews 4:14—16.

1. What does this passage explicitly say about Christ's ability to identify with your struggles?

_____

_____

_____

2. How would your view of Christ be different if you didn't know he suffered as we suffer?

_____

_____

_____

3. Notice that Jesus was "tempted in every way, just as we are." Does that fact give you courage to face your present situation? Why or why not?

_____

_____

_____

4. Do you tend to forget what a privilege it is to be able to take your struggles to God? What is one way you can remind yourself that even when you don't know what to do, you can go to Christ without hesitation?

_____

_____

_____

5. Is this a time of need for you or someone you know? Take your concerns to the Lord with confidence.

_____

_____

_____

_____

☐ Pray the "I Believe" Prayer (see p. 7).

☐ Make "I believe" statements.

☐ Track daily joys on pages 40–41.

☐ Take your third step to remove clutter from your life.

☐ Read chapter 7 in *When Life Becomes a Maze.*

DAY 46 · *Wednesday, Date* _____

 **·TODAY'S· PROMISE** ▶ **Hebrews 2:18**

Read Hebrews 2:14—18.

1. According to these verses, why did Christ take on a human body? How does knowing Christ was fully man shape your view of him as Savior?

_____

_____

_____

2. Review the passage and look for ways Christ is able to sympathize with us as human beings. Which is most meaningful in your current situation?

_____

_____

_____

3. Think about the ways Christ suffered in his last week of life. Consider his betrayal, loneliness, rejection, being misunderstood, humiliation, agony, and death (see Matthew 26—27). Which of these kinds of suffering are you most able to identify with? Explain.

_____

_____

_____

4. What is the greatest area of confusion in your life presently? Why not spend a few moments in prayer. Thank God for his love and care for you, knowing that Christ relates to your problem and desires to help you through your maze.

_____

_____

_____

_____

☐ Pray the "I Believe" Prayer (see p. 7).

☐ Make "I believe" statements.

☐ Give joy to someone (record this on pp. 40—41).

☐ Take your third step to remove clutter from your life.

☐ Decide whether or not to continue meeting with your prayer partners.

☐ Read chapter 7 in *When Life Becomes a Maze.*

Day 47

Thursday, Date _____   Topic 8 runs Thursday through Sunday, Days 47–50.

 Pray
Lord, please be about your work whether I understand it or not.

 Read
Read John 16:16–20.

 Reflect
These words of Jesus were confusing to his disciples. In fact, for some days those closest to the Lord had struggled to understand what was going on. And things would get worse before they got better.

In typical fashion, Christ didn't attempt to explain everything God was doing. He just assured the Twelve that their grief would turn to joy, their mourning would become rejoicing.

What an understatement that was!

Once again God would reveal himself to be the absolute master of surprising outcomes! But the Twelve would have to wait a bit longer before the reality of this incredible promise would be realized.

While most people aren't very good at waiting, our Lord is quite adept at coming up with unexpected solutions to our supposedly unsolvable problems.

 Apply
Jesus spoke these words in the Upper Room before his arrest. How would the events of the next three days show the difference between human expectations and God's plans (see John 18–20)?

_____

What is a surprising outcome you have witnessed in your life? How can that encourage you to trust God for the future? In what specific situation do you need to trust him for a surprising outcome today?

_____

_____

In verse 22 Jesus tells his disciples that when he sees them again they will be filled with joy that no one can take away. Do you believe joy like that is available for you? Has tracking daily joys helped you see that joy can be a permanent part of your life? Why or why not?

_____

_____

 Pray
Pray the "I Believe" Prayer (see p. 7).

·TODAY'S· PROMISE   1 Corinthians 1:25

Read 1 Corinthians 1:18—31.

1. According to this passage how has God's plan of salvation through Jesus' death and resurrection turned the wisdom of the world upside down?

_____

_____

2. James 1:5 says, "If any of you lacks wisdom, he should ask God . . . and it will be given to him." In what specific area of your life do you need to ignore the world's wisdom and find God's wisdom? What step can you take to do that?

_____

_____

3. Sometimes we expect God to respond to our needs according to our own agenda. What is one area of your life in which you can set aside your expectations and trust God to work in a surprising way?

_____

_____

4. Read 1 Corinthians 2:9—10. Just as God brought salvation to the world in a surprising way, he also brings surprising outcomes to situations in our lives. Based on that confidence, what "I believe" statement can you make today?

_____

_____

5. Today's readings show that salvation doesn't come through human works or wisdom. Think about your salvation and what it cost God. Then spend a few moments in worship before the Lord.

☐ Pray the "I Believe" Prayer (see p. 7).

☐ Make "I believe" statements.

☐ Track daily joys on pages 40—41.

☐ Take your third step to remove clutter from your life.

☐ Decide whether or not to continue meeting with your prayer partners.

☐ Read chapter 8 in *When Life Becomes a Maze.*

● DAY 49 *Saturday, Date* _____

Read John 20:1—18.

1. What three words do you suppose might describe the mood of Jesus' disciples after the Crucifixion?

_____

_____

_____

2. In what ways would the time between Jesus' crucifixion and his resurrection have been incredibly confusing for his followers? Do you think they expected Jesus to rise from the grave? Explain.

_____

_____

_____

3. Mary's grief in verses 10–14 changed to joy after recognizing the risen Lord. What is a time during this Adventure when you recognized Christ's presence in your life and responded with joy? How can you continue to be aware of the Lord's presence and the joy he provides after this Adventure?

_____

_____

_____

4. What does the Resurrection say about God's power? How does this affect the way you view your present circumstances?

_____

_____

_____

5. What is a confusing situation in your life? What is one step you can take to place your hope in the God of surprising outcomes?

_____

_____

_____

☐ Pray the "I Believe" Prayer (see p. 7).

☐ Make "I believe" statements.

☐ Track daily joys on pages 40–41.

☐ Take your third step to remove clutter from your life.

☐ Decide whether or not to continue meeting with your prayer partners.

☐ Read chapter 8 in *When Life Becomes a Maze*.

AY 50 *Sunday, Date* _____

Read John 20:19—31.

Why do you think Thomas doubted the other disciples? If the disciples had told Thomas simply that Jesus' body was stolen, do you think he would have believed that? it easier to believe things that have natural explanations rather than supernatural? Why or why not?

_____
_____
_____

Jesus is risen. Do you believe that? Do you live as if you believe it? What is one way you can continue to be an "I believe" person beyond this Adventure?

_____
_____
_____

Finish this sentence with what you would like to remember about these 50 days: *When I don't know what to do . . .*

_____
_____
_____
_____

Jesus said to Thomas, "Because you have seen me, you have believed; blessed are those who have not seen and yet have believed." What is one way you can celebrate the privilege of being one of Christ's "I believe" people today?

_____
_____
_____
_____

How have you grown during this Adventure? What action steps would you like to continue in the days ahead?

_____
_____
_____
_____
_____
_____

Don't miss the follow-up day on page 75.

LOOKING · BACK ·

LOOKING · AHEAD ·

Check the box if you have completed the assignment.

☐ I have completed most of Days I–50.

☐ I have prayed the "I Believe" Prayer.

☐ I have filled my days with "I believe" statements.

☐ I have tracked my daily joys.

☐ I have met four times with my prayer partners.

☐ I have removed clutter from my life in three specific ways.

☐ I have read *When Life Becomes a Maze.*

Optional Follow-up Scriptures for Extra Study on Topics 7 and 8:
I Peter 2:24–25
Matthew 28
Luke 24:13–35
Acts 2:14,22–32

Suggestions:

● Complete Day 5I on page 75.

● Continue to study Scripture and pray daily.

● Continue to make "I believe" statements.

● Continue to track your daily joys.

● Continue to meet with your prayer partners.

● Continue to unclutter your life.

Continue the Adventure All Year Long!

Scripture Union devotionals are the perfect way to maintain the healthy spiritual habits of daily Scripture reading and prayer after the Adventure is over. The topic introduction days in this Adventure (usually Saturday/Sunday) were patterned after the Scripture Union guides. And on the next page we have provided you with a sample from Scripture Union's *Discovery* as a follow-up day. For more information on Scripture Union devotionals for all ages, see page 76.

Pray

Lord, I don't want circumstances to determine whether my life brings praise to you. Help me to honor you each day no matter what happens.

Read

When trapped in a difficult or confusing situation, Christians sometimes minimize what Jesus can do for them. Paul's letter to the Colossians is about an entire congregation which thought less of Christ than it should have. Keep this in mind as you begin reading through this short epistle.

NOW READ COLOSSIANS 1:1–14.

Reflect

Churches have personalities just as people do. Some are aggressive and Christ-centered, while others appear more provincial and self-centered. Think back on various congregations you have been a part of and you will probably agree that this is true.

The Christians Paul wrote to at Colosse had a fatal flaw. They thought less of Christ than they should have. They knew he could forgive sin, but that was about all they saw him capable of doing. So they were looking for additional help from whatever source they could find. All this resulted in their living lives unworthy of the Lord.

In verse 10 Paul addresses this issue early on when he states in essence: "And we pray this in order that you may lead a life worthy of who Jesus is." In the paragraphs which follow, the apostle will speak about the wonder of who Jesus is.

How any of us lives as a Christian is directly related to what our convictions about Christ really are.

Apply

Who are people at your church who live lives worthy of the Lord? Why do you feel this way about them? What about your family—would Christ say your lives are a good reflection of all he has done in your behalf? What would Jesus say by way of commendation about how you personally live out your faith?

Pray

Lord, help me to live a life worthy of all you have done in my behalf.

To order Discovery *or other age-graded Scripture Union devotional resources, see the order form on page 76.*

● You've Finished the Adventure—Now What?

It's time to make a lifestyle out of growing spiritually!

HEALTHY SPIRITUAL habits like daily Scripture reading and prayer have been a part of your life for the past 50 days. Don't let them stop now! Though the Adventure has ended, the disciplines you've developed don't need to. Rather, you can make spiritual growth a consistent pattern that can last a lifetime!

Consider using a Scripture Union devotional guide to maintain the spiritual habits you've practiced throughout the 50-Day Adventure. You can benefit from these devotionals all year round. In fact, you've already used the Scripture Union format with the topic introduction pages in this journal.

There are Scripture Union devotionals for people of all ages. *Quest* is available for children ages 7–10. *One to One* is for youth ages 11–14. *Discovery* is a personal application guide for mature young people and adults, and *Encounter with God* is an advanced Bible study guide for experienced Christians, teachers, and leaders.

Scripture Union and The Chapel Ministries are dedicated to encouraging the daily study of God's Word. That's why we've teamed up to help people like you develop a strong relationship with God through regular Bible study. So take up the challenge of making healthy spiritual habits last all year long.

SEE PREVIEW OPTION BELOW

You may order Scripture Union devotionals for yourself, your family, or for friends by calling The Chapel Ministries at 1-800-224-2735 or by filling out the order form below and mailing it with your check

☐ Yes! I would like to order an annual subscription. (Check all that apply.)
☐ OR: Please send me preview copies for $1.00 each. (Check your choices—one copy per title.)

	Price	Qty	Total Amt
☐ Discovery (adult application)	$20.00	____	_____
☐ Encounter with God (adult study)	$20.00	____	_____
☐ One to One (ages 11–14)	$20.00	____	_____
☐ Quest (ages 7–10)	$20.00	____	_____
☐ Preview copies	$ 1.00 ea.	____	_____

_____ Grand Total Enclosed

Please provide the information below:
Your name _____
Address _____ City _____
State/Prov _____ Zip/Code _____ Phone (___) _____
Make checks payable to: The Chapel Ministries

Send this order form to:
The Chapel Ministries, Box 30, Wheaton, IL 60189-0030.
Or call 1-800-224-2735 (in Canada 1-800-461-4114) for credit card orders.   SUGJ96

All devotionals will be sent every three months for one year.

The Chapel Ministries Wants to Hear from You!

Y OUR FEEDBACK helps us evaluate the effectiveness of the 50-Day Spiritual Adventure ministry. Please fill out this comment form and tell us what God did in your life, church, or small group during this 50-day journey. In return for your feedback we would like to say "thanks" by sending you one of the free books shown on the next page. Simply choose the one you'd like to receive!

Tell us a story of how this Adventure has changed your life or the life of your church or small group.

_____
_____
_____
_____
_____
_____
_____
_____
_____
_____
_____
_____
_____

How can we improve the 50-Day Adventures for you?

_____
_____
_____
_____
_____
_____
_____
_____
_____

How were you involved in the 50-Day Adventure? (Check all that apply.)
☐ Individual ☐ Sunday school class ☐ Small group
☐ Family ☐ Entire church ☐ Other _____

Did you tune in to any of the Adventure programs on the "You Need to Know" television program? ☐ Yes ☐ No

For your FREE "thank you" book turn to the next page!

Choose Your Free Book!

☐ 101 Ways to Simplify Your Life
☐ 8 Survival Skills for Changing Times

Fill out the information below:

Name _____

Address _____

City _____ State/Prov _____ Zip/Code _____

Church name and city _____

TV station where you watch "You Need to Know" _____

Periodically we include Adventure testimonies in our newsletters and mailings. May we contact you for more information about your story? _____

Phone (_____) _____

Mail this comment form to:

      The Chapel Ministries, Box 30, Wheaton, IL 60189-0030

      In Canada: Box 2000, Waterdown, ON L0R 2H0

      Or e-mail us your comments at: T50DSA.aol.com

FBC96

If this Adventure has helped you develop healthy spiritual habits, then why not use these other 50-Day Adventures from The Chapel Ministries.

Facing Down Our Fears
Finding Courage When Anxiety Grips the Heart

Are there areas in your life where you feel afraid? We're all afraid of something, but don't give up just yet! In this 50-Day Spiritual Adventure you'll find practical and biblical suggestions for finding courage and over-coming fear.

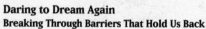

Facing Down Our Fears Adult Journal and
How to Fear God Without Being Afraid of Him necessary book—$10 for both

Daring to Dream Again
Breaking Through Barriers That Hold Us Back

God has big dreams for us, but sometimes we lose sight of his great plans. Through this 50-Day Spiritual Adventure you will find solutions to problems that can keep you from living God's dreams. This journal features simple, achievable suggestions for overcoming those hindrances—so that God's dreams for you can become reality.

Daring to Dream Again Adult Journal and
How to Be a World Class Christian necessary book—$10 for both

Survival Skills for Changing Times
Purposeful Christian Living in the '90s

As Christians we don't need to be overcome by the complexities of life in the '90s. Through this 50-Day Spiritual Adventure, you'll explore specific skills found in Scripture that will help you survive—and thrive—in our culture today.

Survival Skills Adult Journal and
Getting Beyond "How Are You" necessary book—$10 for both

4-Week Worship Celebration
We Will Glorify: Becoming People of Worship in Church and Home

Do you hunger for God in the midst of your daily activities? Through action steps, family activities, Bible study, historical insights, and an Agape Celebration, this 4-week series will help you live a life of worship.

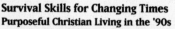

We Will Glorify Personal Worship Journal and
Putting God in His Place supplementary book—$10
An Agape Celebration with Twila Paris video (for a home worship experience)—$10

Request your copies of these Chapel Ministries resources today. Use the order form on page 80 in this journal for convenient home delivery, or ask for this resource at your church or local Christian bookstore.

● The Chapel Ministries Resources Order Form

Item	Title *(Take advantage of the discounts below)*	Retail	Discount	Quantity	Total
2610	Adult Journal	6.00	*	___	___
2620	Student Journal	6.00	*	___	___
2630	Children's Journal	6.00	*	___	___
2640	Critter County Activity Book	6.00	*	___	___
450S	Critter County Scripture Memory Tape	6.00	*	___	___
1761	When Life Becomes a Maze	6.00	*	___	___
450U	When Life Becomes a Maze audiobook	12.00	*	___	___
7772	Believe It Or Not Scripture Promise Pack	1.00	*	___	___
1762	Don't Die in the Winter	7.99	6.50	___	___
1763	Two Are Better Than One	4.99	4.00	___	___
1764	When God Whispers	9.99	8.00	___	___
1765	Margin	12.00	10.00	___	___
1766	If I'm Forgiven, Why Do I Still Feel Guilty?	8.99	7.50	___	___
1777	He Still Moves Stones	12.99	10.50	___	___
8419	Veggie Tales: God Wants Me to Forgive Them?!? video	14.95	12.00	___	___
5689	Facing Down Our Fears Adult Journal and book	10.00	*	___	___
5690	Daring to Dream Again Adult Journal and book	10.00	*	___	___
5691	Survival Skills Adult Journal and book	10.00	*	___	___
5694	We Will Glorify Personal Worship Journal and book	10.00	*	___	___
8403	Agape Celebration video	10.00	*	___	___

Subtotal _____

Add 10% for UPS shipping/handling ($4.00 minimum) _____

Canadian or Illinois residents add 7% GST/sales tax _____

Total (subtotal + shipping + tax) _____

Here's my donation to help support the work of The Chapel Ministries _____

TOTAL AMOUNT ENCLOSED _____

Ship my order to:

Name _____

Street Address* _____ City _____

State/Prov _____ Zip/Code _____ Phone (___) _____

*(Note: UPS will not deliver to a PO box)

I watch "You Need to Know" on television station _____

Mail this order form with your check made payable to:
The Chapel Ministries, Box 30, Wheaton, IL 60189-0030
In Canada: Box 2000, Waterdown, ON L0R 2H0

For U.S. Visa, MasterCard, or Discover card orders call 1-800-224-2735.
In Canada call 1-800-461-4114.

ABC96